Grade 1

Treasures

Practice Book A

Mc Graw Hill **Macmillan McGraw-Hill**

The **McGraw·Hill** Companies

Mc
Graw
Hill **Macmillan**
McGraw-Hill

Published by Macmillan/McGraw-Hill, of McGraw-Hill Education, a division of The McGraw-Hill Companies, Inc.,
Two Penn Plaza, New York, New York 10121.

Printed in the United States of America

4 5 6 7 8 9 10 024 09 08 07

Contents

Unit 2 • Outside My Door

© Macmillan/McGraw-Hill

Unit 3 • Let's Connect

Unit 4 • Our Earth

Unit 5 • I Can Do It!

Unit 6 • Let's Discover

Name _____

Look at the picture. The letter **a** stands for the middle sound in **hat**.

Write the letter <u>a</u> to complete each word. Draw a line from each picture to its name.

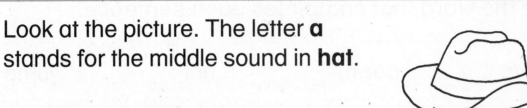

1. c ___ t

2. m ___ t

3. m ___ n

4. p ___ n

© Macmillan/McGraw-Hill

At Home: Have your child write one more word that has the same vowel sound as *hat*.

Pam and Sam • **Book 1.1/Unit 1**

 1

Name _____

Write the word that completes each sentence.

| up | down | not | jump |

_____

1. The cat can _____.

_____

2. The cat is _____.

_____

3. The cat is _____.

_____

4. The cat is _____ sad.

 At Home: Read aloud each word in the box, one at a time. Have your child act out each word.

Name _____

As you read <u>Pam and Sam</u>, fill in the Character Chart.

Pam Can	Sam Can

How does the Character Chart help you remember the beginning, middle, and end of <u>Pam and Sam</u>?

At Home: Have your child use the chart to retell the story.

The **characters** are the people or animals in a story.

Circle each picture that could be a character in a story.

1.

2.

3.

4.

5.

6.

Make up a character. Then draw it.

 At Home: Ask your child to tell you a short story about one of the people or animals shown on the page.

© Macmillan/McGraw-Hill

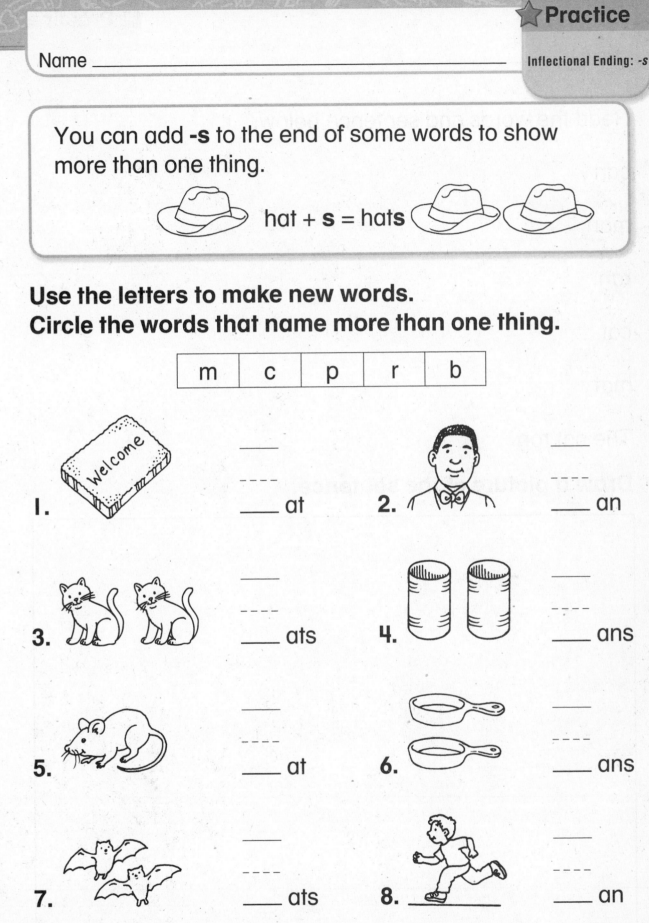
You can add **-s** to the end of some words to show more than one thing.

hat + **s** = hat**s**

Use the letters to make new words.
Circle the words that name more than one thing.

m	c	p	r	b

1. _____ at

2. _____ an

3. _____ ats

4. _____ ans

5. _____ at

6. _____ ans

7. _____ ats

8. _____ an

At Home: Ask your child to say a sentence for three of the newly made words.

Pam and Sam • Book 1.1/Unit 1   5

Read the words and sentence below.

can

man

ran

cat

mat

The cat ran.

Draw a picture of the sentence.

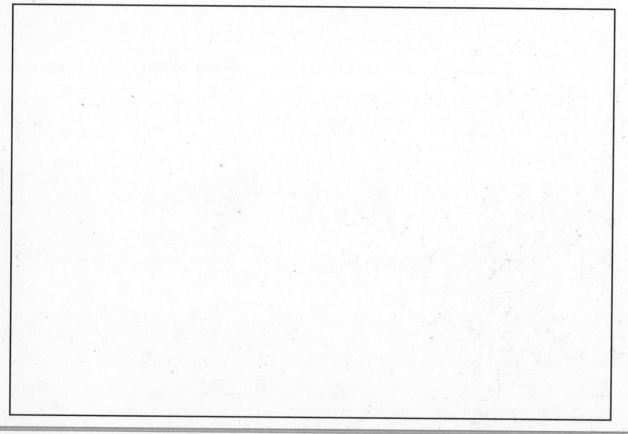

© Macmillan/McGraw-Hill

 At Home: Help your child read the words and sentence above.

Name _____

> **Photographs** are pictures that show people, animals, or things in real life.

Look at the picture.

1. Circle the cat.

2. Put an X on the girl jumping.

3. Put a check mark (√) on the dog.

4. Color the picture to make it look real.

© Macmillan/McGraw-Hill

 At Home: Use a magazine photo to discuss how information is presented in a visual way.

Pam and Sam • **Book 1.1/Unit 1** 7

Put an <u>a</u> on each line to make a word.

p__n   b__t   r__n   h__t   m__t

Look at each picture.
Use the words in the box to complete the sentences.

1. Sam _____ to the van.

2. The cat is in the _____.

3. She sees the _____.

4. The _____ is on the _____.

At Home: Help your child think of rhyming words that go with the words in the box.

Name _____

The letter **a** stands for the middle sound in **man** and **van**.

Write the letter a to complete the words. Draw a line from each picture to its name.

1. m ___ p

2. h ___ t

3. P ___ m

4. b ___ g

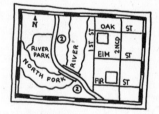

© Macmillan/McGraw-Hill

 At Home: Have your child write one more word that has the same vowel sound as *cap*.

Use a word from the box to complete each sentence.

over	Yes	it	too

1. She can bat _____.

2. Dan can bat, _____.

3. _____, I can jump up!

4. No! It is _____ the !

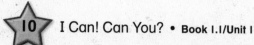
At Home: Have your child think of another sentence using one of the words in the box.

© Macmillan/McGraw-Hill

As you read I Can! Can You?, fill in the Sequence Chart.

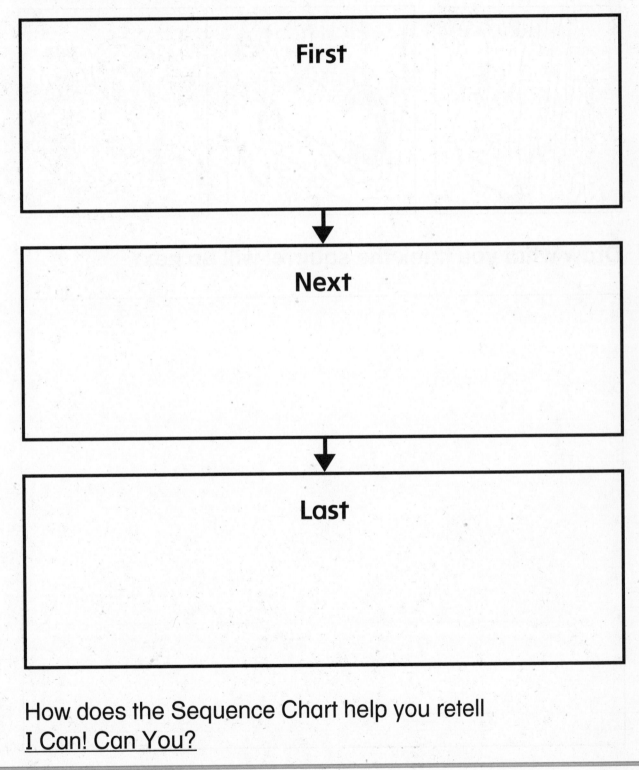

First

Next

Last

How does the Sequence Chart help you retell
I Can! Can You?

At Home: Have your child use the chart to retell the story.

Look at the pictures. Write 1, 2, and 3 to show the order in which things happen.

Draw what you think the squirrel will do next.

At Home: Ask your child to tell you a story, pointing to the pictures in order. Ask: *What happens first? What happens next? What happens last?*

© Macmillan/McGraw-Hill

Name _____

Write the letter <u>a</u> to complete the words.
Then add <u>-s</u> to the end of each word.
Draw a line from each word to its picture.

___ ___
- - -   - - -

1. f ___ n ___

___ ___
- - -   - - -

2. n ___ p ___

___ ___
- - -   - - -

3. t ___ p ___

___ ___
- - -   - - -

4. t ___ g ___

___ ___
- - -   - - -

5. p ___ t ___

At Home: Help your child make up a sentence using one of
the words above.

I Can! Can You? • **Book 1.1/Unit 1**   13

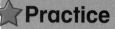
Read the words and sentence below.

tap

sad

nap

dad

over

Dad can tap it over.

Draw a picture of the sentence.

 At Home: Help your child read the words and sentence above.

Name _____

Labels tell about things in a picture.

Use the labels to write the names for the pictures.

1. _____

2. _____

3. _____

4. _____

 At Home: Have your child think of labels to put on things in
your home.

I Can! Can You? • **Book 1.1/Unit 1** 15

Circle the pictures if you hear the sound of short <u>a</u>.

1.

2.

3.

4.

5.

6.

7.

8.

9.

 At Home: Help your child to recognize the short *a* sound in the name of things in your home.

Name _____

The letter **i** stands for the middle sound in **big** and **sit**.

Write the letter i to complete the word.
Draw a line from each picture to its name.

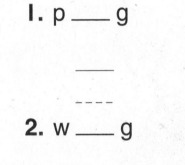

1. p __ g

2. w __ g

3. p __ n

4. k __ d

5. b __ b

 At Home: Have your child write one word that has the same vowel sound as *big*.

Name _____

Read the words in the box.

| Run | run | be | ride |

Circle the word that completes each sentence.
Then write the word on the line.

_____

- - - - - - - - - - -

1. Sam can _____ up and down.

ride   run

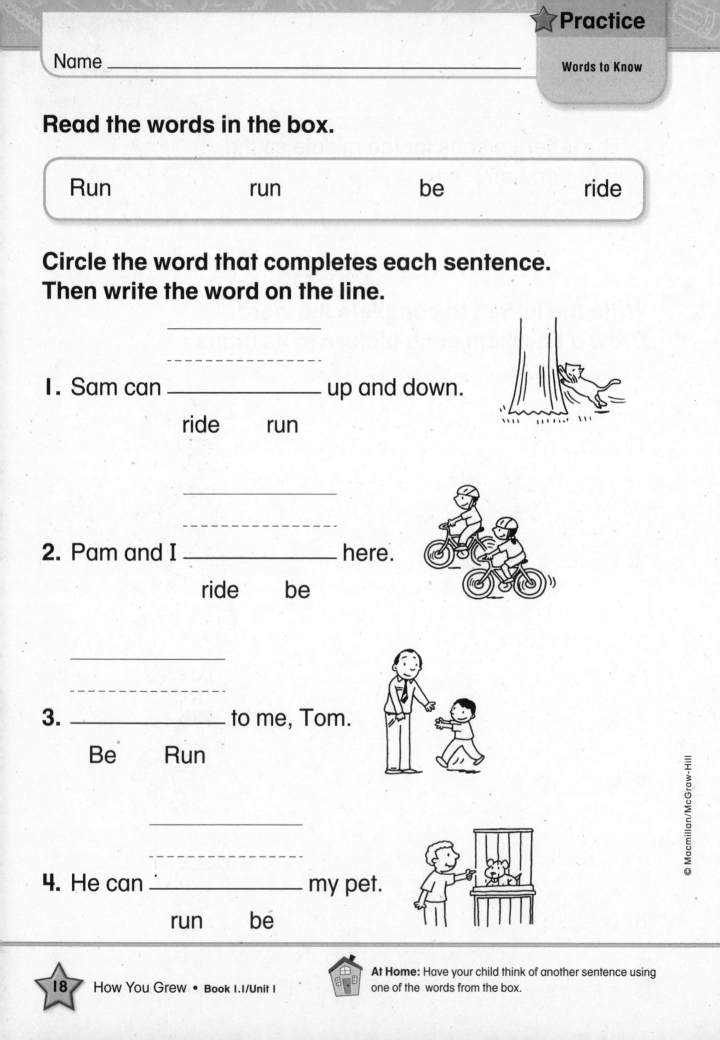

_____

- - - - - - - - - - -

2. Pam and I _____ here.

ride   be

_____

- - - - - - - - - - -

3. _____ to me, Tom.

Be   Run

_____

- - - - - - - - - - -

4. He can _____ my pet.

run   be

At Home: Have your child think of another sentence using one of the words from the box.

© Macmillan/McGraw-Hill

Name _____

As you read <u>How You Grew</u>, fill in the
Sequence Chart.

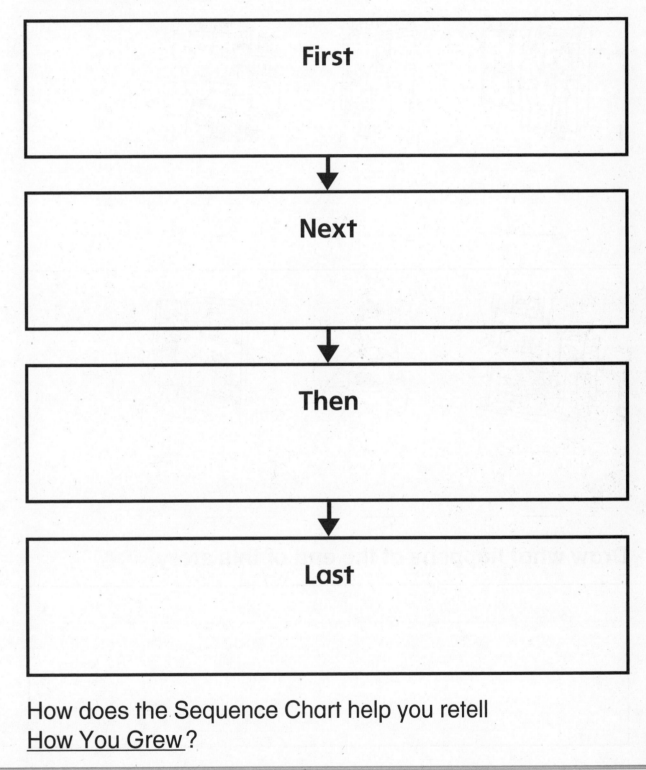

First

↓

Next

↓

Then

↓

Last

How does the Sequence Chart help you retell
<u>How You Grew</u>?

 At Home: Have your child use the chart to retell the story.

Name _____

Look at the pictures. Write <u>1</u>, <u>2</u>, and <u>3</u> to show what happened <u>first</u>, <u>next</u>, and <u>last</u>.

1.

_____   _____   _____

- - - -   - - - -   - - - -

_____   _____   _____

2.

_____   _____   _____

- - - -   - - - -   - - - -

_____   _____   _____

Draw what happens at the end of this story.

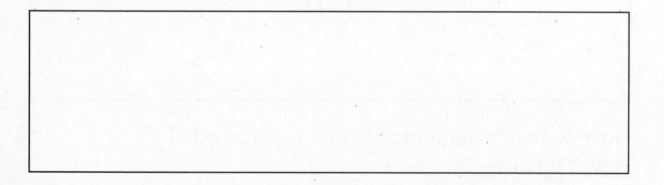

 At Home: Have your child describe in order what is happening in each picture.

Name _____

Some words end in the same two consonants.

Bi**ll**   mi**tt**   pa**ss**

Read each group of words.
Find the word that ends in the same two
consonant letters.
Write the word on the line.

1. hill   hat   ham   _____

2. pen   kiss   can   _____

3. bat   top   Jill   _____

4. Matt   pup   cap   _____

At Home: Have your child use one of the answers in a sentence. Have your child name the double consonant at the end of the word.

How You Grew • **Book 1.1/Unit 1**

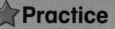
Name _____

Read the words and sentence below.

run

hit

sit

miss

big

I can run fast.

Draw a picture of the sentence.

At Home: Help your child read the words and sentence above.

Name _____

The **title** of a book is the name of the book.
The **author** of a book writes the story.
The **illustrator** makes the pictures.

Use the book cover to complete the sentences.

1. The title of the book is _____.

2. The author of the book is _____.

3. The illustrator of the book is _____.

4. The _____ writes the story.

5. The _____ makes the pictures.

🏠 **At Home:** Have your child point to the title, author, and illustrator of the book. Talk about what could happen in this book.

How You Grew • **Book 1.1/Unit 1**   23

Write a word from the box to finish the sentence

dig	pig	hid	bib

1. The man can _____.

2. He has a big _____.

3. The pig has a _____.

4. The pig _____ it.

Draw a picture of what could happen next.

 At Home: Have your child make up a story about the man and the pig.

© Macmillan/McGraw-Hill

Name _____

Look at the pictures.
Blend the first two letters to read each word.

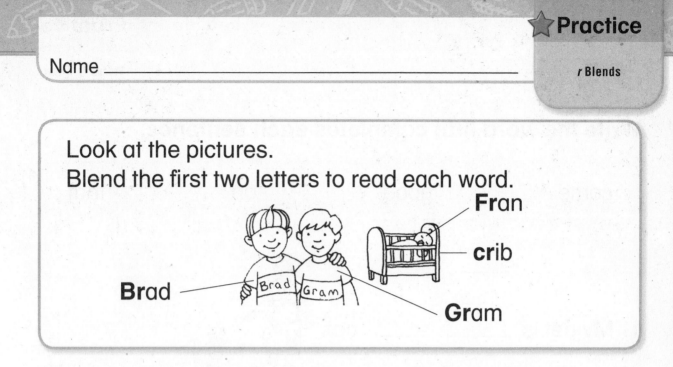

Fran

crib

Brad

Gram

Use the blends <u>br</u>, <u>gr</u>, <u>tr</u> or <u>cr</u> to complete the words. Draw a line from each word to its picture.

1. _____in

2. _____ap

3. _____ab

4. _____ick

At Home: Have your child write another word that begins with each *r* blend: *br, tr, gr,* and *cr.*

Name _____

Write the word that completes each sentence.

come	good	on	that

1. My pet is _____ cat.

2. My pet can do a _____ trick!

3. My pet sits _____ me!

4. My pet will _____ to me.

5. What pet is _____ for you?

At Home: Have your child think of another sentence using one of the words in the box.

As you read Pet Tricks, fill in the Setting Chart.

Setting	What the Characters Do There

How does the Setting Chart help you retell Pet Tricks?

 At Home: Have your child use the chart to retell the story.

Pet Tricks • Book1.1/Unit 1   27

Name _____

Comprehension:
Character and Setting

> The **characters** are the people or animals in a story.
> The **setting** is where the story happens.

Read the story. Then answer the questions.
Draw a picture for each part of the story.

Pam has a cat.
The cat is Sam.

Pam naps.
Sam is sad.

Pam plays with Sam.
Sam is not sad.
Sam likes to play.

_____

1. Who are the characters? _____

_____

2. What is Sam? _____

_____

3. Where are Sam and Pam? _____

_____

4. What does Sam like to do? _____

© Macmillan/McGraw-Hill

At Home: Ask your child to tell about the character(s) and
setting in his or her favorite story.

Name _____

When **'s** is added to a word, it means that something belongs to that person or thing.

Dad**'s** cat

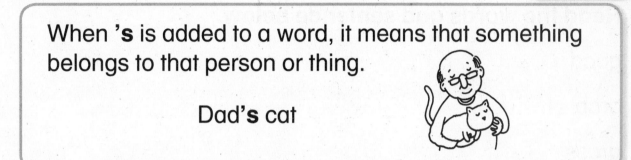

Add <u>'s</u> to show someone has something.

Draw a line to the picture.

____
\- \- \- \-

1. Jim_____ cat

____
\- \- \- \-

2. Matt_____ pet

____
\- \- \- \-

3. Brad_____ bat

____
\- \- \- \-

4. Fran_____ crib

____
\- \- \- \-

5. Will_____ cap

At Home: Ask your child to draw a picture of some of his or her favorite things. Then talk about the picture using the possessive form of 's.

Name _____

Read the words and sentence below.

good

grab

grass

that

trap

That cat is in the grass.

Draw a picture of the sentence.

 At Home: Help your child read the words and sentence above.

© Macmillan/McGraw-Hill

Name _____

A **list** is a series of things written in order.

Pets can:

1. jump

2. play

3. nap

Write the word that completes the sentence.

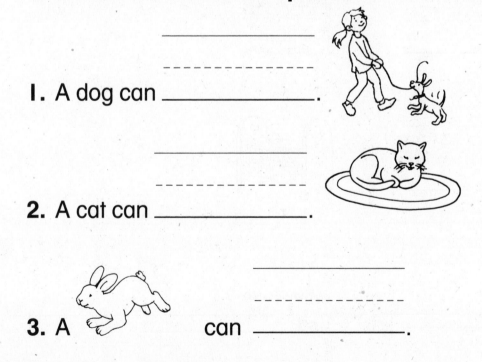

1. A dog can _____.

2. A cat can _____.

3. A _____ can _____.

© Macmillan/McGraw-Hill

Name _____

Look at each picture.
Write the word that tells about the picture.

| crib | brick | crab | grass | track |

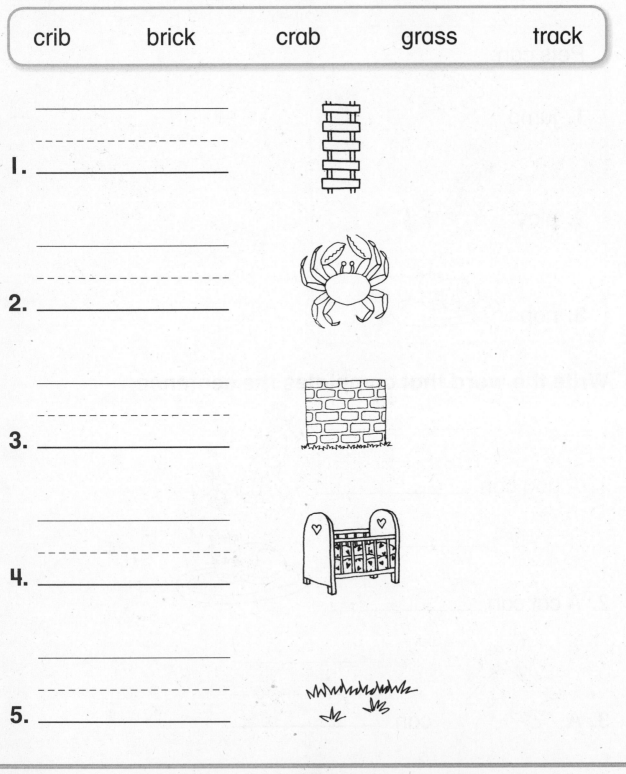

1. _____

2. _____

3. _____

4. _____

5. _____

 At Home: Ask your child to find a toy that starts with *cr, br,* or *tr.*

Words that end with letter blends have the sounds of both letters.

n + t = nt   a **n t**   l i **s t**   s i **n k**

Say the word each picture shows.
Write the letter blends at the end of each word.
You can write nd, st, nt, or nk.

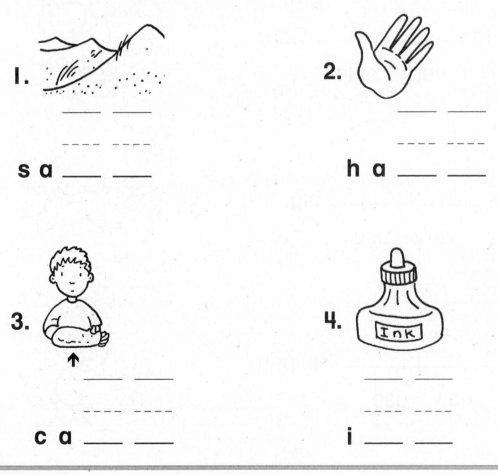

1. _ _ _ _
    s a ___ ___

2. _ _ _ _
    h a ___ ___

3. _ _ _ _
    c a ___ ___

4. _ _ _ _
    i ___ ___

 At Home: Have your child write another word that has the same end sound as *land*, *last*, *mint*, and *pink*.

Name _____

Circle the word that completes each sentence.
Then write the word on the line.

very	help	use	now

1. We can ride _____.

       use   now

2. Pat likes to _____ Sam.

      very   help

3. My dog is _____ big.

      very   use

4. Nat can _____ that pen.

      now   use

© Macmillan/McGraw-Hill

 At Home: Ask your child to make up a sentence using one of the words in the box.

Name _____

As you read <u>Soccer</u>, fill in the Author's Purpose Chart.

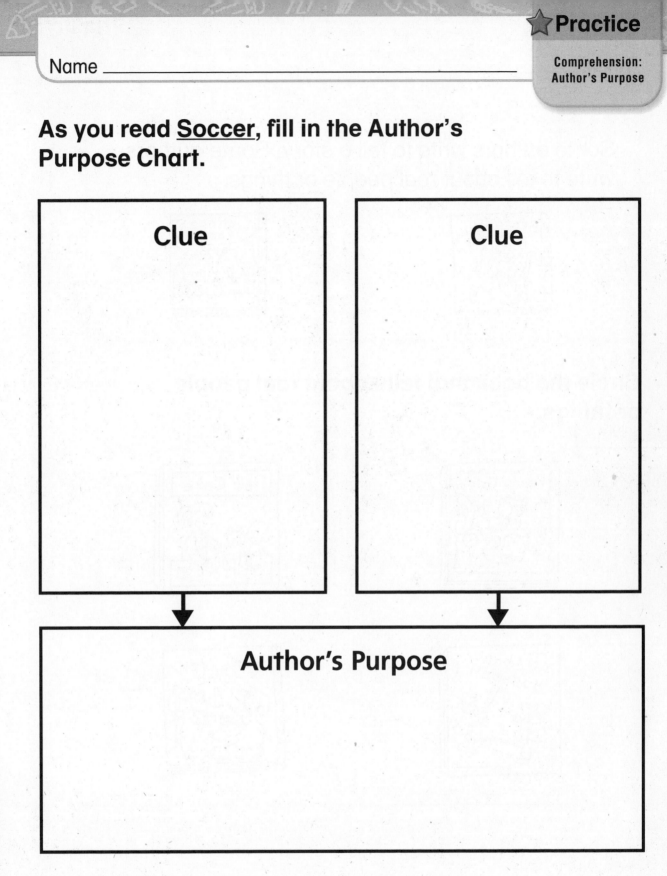

Clue	Clue

Author's Purpose

How does the Author's Purpose Chart help you understand the story <u>Soccer</u>?

© Macmillan/McGraw-Hill

At Home: Have your child use the chart to retell the story.

Soccer • **Book 1.1/Unit 1** **35**

Some authors write to tell a story. Some authors write to tell about real people or things.

Circle the book that tells about real people or things.

At Home: Have your child name a book that tells a story and a book that gives facts about something.

© Macmillan/McGraw-Hill

Name _____

Read each group of words.
Find the word with the <u>final blend</u> in it.

Write the word on the line.

1. 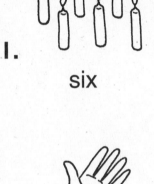         _____

six   sink   sun

2.    _____

hand   toy   Tom

3. _____

hat   hop   tent

4.          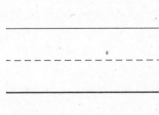   _____

cast   Nan   nut

At Home: Have your child write another word that ends in *nd*, *st*, *nt*, or *nk*. Identify the CVCC letter pattern in the word.

© Macmillan/McGraw-Hill

Read the words and sentence below.

help

land

sand

fast

very

I run very fast.

Draw a picture of the sentence.

At Home: Help your child read the words and sentence above.

Name _____

Words often rhyme in a poem.

Rhyming words begin with different sounds and end with the same sound.   m**an**   c**an**

Say each pair of sentences. Circle the rhyming words. Write the words on the line.

1.  Pam has a fan.

It is very tan.

_____

_____

2.  Where do you see Bill?

Look! He is on that hill.

_____

_____

3.  Sam can be mad.

Now Sam is bad.

_____

_____

4.  Lin can hit.

Up and down a bit!

_____

_____

© Macmillan/McGraw-Hill

Name _____

| last | ant | hand | sand | band | bank |

Look at the pictures. Write the correct word in each box.

 At Home: Look through some magazines with your child.
See if you can find any items that end with *nd, st, nt,* or *nk.*

Name _____

Circle the words that tell about the picture.

1. jump on   ride in

2. very big   too little

3. not good   can drink

4. come down   go up

5. run up   help Dad

6. that cat   runs now

Circle the word that completes the sentence.

1.

Wags can ___ in.

yes   run

2.

Jim will go ___ now.

down   up

3.

I can ___ this.

use   you

4.

What is in ___?

it   an

5.

The cat jumps ___ the sink.

not   over

6.

Yes, I can ___ it.

sit   ride

Name _____

Look at the picture. The letter **o** stands for the middle sound in **pot**.

pot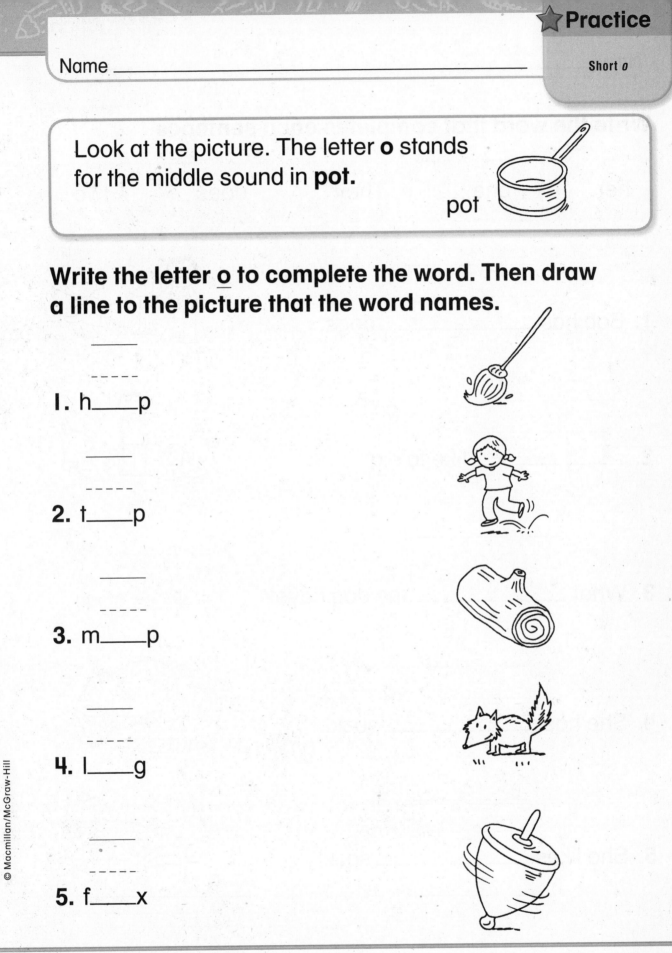

Write the letter o to complete the word. Then draw a line to the picture that the word names.

1. h___p

2. t___p

3. m___p

4. l___g

5. f___x

 At Home: Have your child write another word that has the same vowel sound as in *pot*.

Animal Moms and Dads
Book 1.2/Unit 2

43

© Macmillan/McGraw-Hill

Name _____

Write the word that completes each sentence.

| her | one | They | does | two |

1. Bob has _____ dogs.

2. _____ like to dig.

3. What _____ the dog have?

4. She has _____ sock!

5. She likes _____ sock!

 At Home: Have your child think of another sentence using one of the words in the box.

Name _____

As you read <u>Animal Moms and Dads</u>, fill in the Main Idea and Details Web.

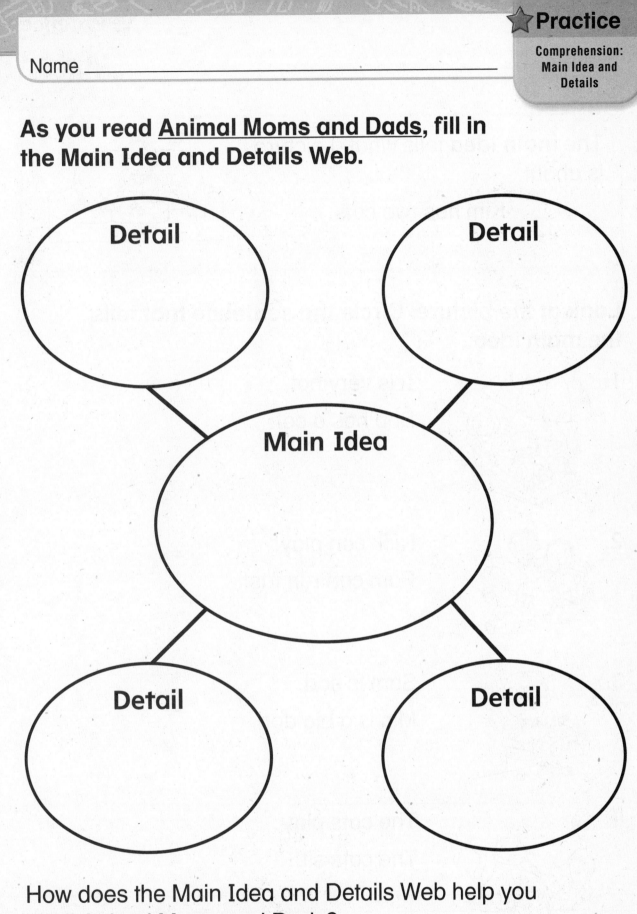

Detail

Detail

Main Idea

Detail

Detail

How does the Main Idea and Details Web help you retell <u>Animal Moms and Dads?</u>

 At Home: Have your child use the web to retell the story.

Name _____

The **main idea** tells what a picture
is about.

Kim has two cats.

**Look at the picture. Circle the sentence that tells
the main idea.**

1.    It is very hot.

Bob has a cat.

2.    Nick can play.

Pam can run fast.

3.    Sam is sad.

Min is a big dog.

4.    The cats play.

The cats sit.

 At Home: Have your child make up a story about one
of the pictures.

Name _____

You can add **-ed** to some action words to tell what someone or something did.

jump + ed = jumped   Tom jumped up.

Put the two parts together to make a new word.

1. kick + ed = _____

2. pick + ed = _____

3. lock + ed = _____

Now write the two parts of each word.

4. licked = _____ + _____

5. mixed = _____ + _____

6. packed = _____ + _____

At Home: Have your child add *-ed* to the word *walk* and use the new word in a sentence.

Animal Moms and Dads
Book 1.2/Unit 2

47

Name _____

Read the words and sentences below.

hot

log

lot

one

they

The hog is hot.

They have one frog.

Draw a picture of one of the sentences.

 At Home: Help your child read the words and sentences above.

Name _____

Rhythmic patterns are sounds and words that repeat to give a poem a beat.

Read the poem.

One little pig,
Sat on a wig,
He did not play,
He did not dig.

Write three words that rhyme in the poem.

_____

1. _____

2. _____

3. _____

4. Underline three words that repeat in the poem.

 At Home: Clap out the beat of the poem as you and your child read it aloud.

Name _____

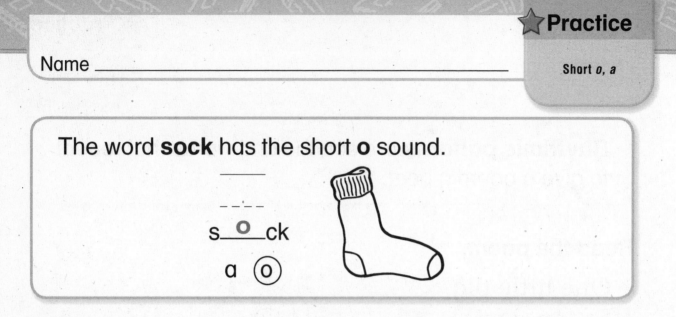

The word **sock** has the short **o** sound.

s__o__ck

a   ⓞ

Circle the letter to complete the picture name.
Then write the letter.

1.

m____p

a   o

2.

h____t

a   o

3.

t____p

a   o

4.

c____t

a   o

Change the letter a to the letter o. Write the new word.

5. hat _____

6. pat _____

At Home: Have your child read the words. Then ask him or her to write another word with the short o sound and draw a picture.

Name _____

Say the name of the picture.

Listen to the sound the letter **e** stands for in **hen** and **bell**.

Write the letter e to complete each word.
Then circle the picture the word names.

1. b___d

2. p___n

3. j___t

4. p___t

5. w___ll

 At Home: Have your child write more words that have the short *e* sound.

Name _____

Write the word that completes each sentence.

Who	some	of	no	eat

1. Do dogs _____ ?

2. Can I pick _____ ?

3. _____ is at the _____ ?

4. The ⬤ is _____ good.

5. Where is the box _____ ?

At Home: Have your child think of another sentence using one of the words in the box.

© Macmillan/McGraw-Hill

Name _____

As you read <u>Little Red Hen</u>, fill in the Retelling Chart.

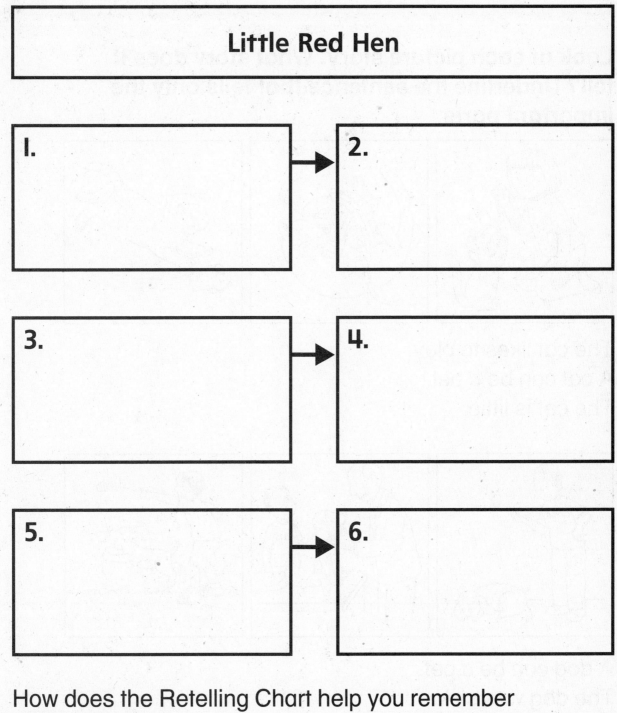

Little Red Hen

1.

2.

3.

4.

5.

6.

How does the Retelling Chart help you remember
<u>Little Red Hen</u>?

At Home: Have your child use the chart to retell the story.

Little Red Hen • **Book 1.2/Unit 2** 53

When you **retell** a story, you tell only the important parts.

Look at each picture story. What story does it tell? Underline the sentence that tells only the important parts.

The cat likes to play.
A cat can be a pet.
The cat is little.

A dog can be a pet.
The dog was sick.
The dog likes to run.

 At Home: Ask your child to tell you what happened after school. Remind your child to tell only the important parts.

Name _____

A **contraction** is a short form of two words. One or more letters are replaced by an **apostrophe (')**.

is + not = **isn't**

The pet **is not** on the bed.

The pet **isn't** on the bed.

Write the contraction for the underlined words.

1. Ted <u>can not</u> run. _____

2. Jen <u>did not</u> play. _____

3. Ben <u>is not</u> here. _____

4. Peg <u>does not</u> have a cat. _____

 At Home: Ask your child to make up a sentence using one of the contractions above.

Little Red Hen • **Book 1.2/Unit 2**   55

Name _____

Read the words and sentences below.

get

some

who

hen

men

Who will help the hen?

Some men will help.

Draw a picture of one of the sentences.

 At Home: Help your child read the words and sentences above.

© Macmillan/McGraw-Hill

Name _____

A **diagram** is a picture that shows the parts of something.

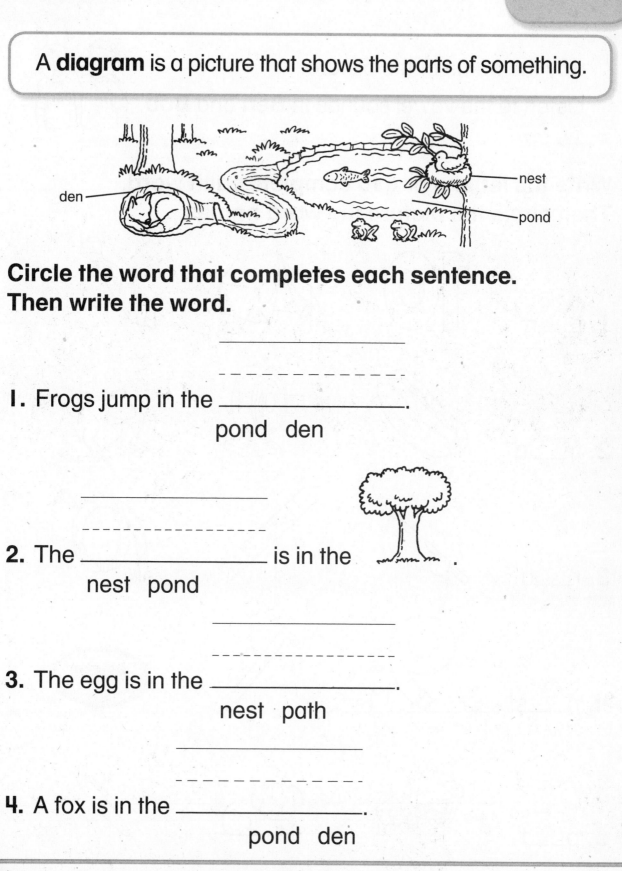

den   nest   pond

**Circle the word that completes each sentence.
Then write the word.**

1. Frogs jump in the _____.

           pond   den

2. The _____ is in the _____.

     nest   pond

3. The egg is in the _____.

           nest   path

4. A fox is in the _____.

           pond   den

© Macmillan/McGraw-Hill

At Home: Have your child think of other animals to add to the diagram. Then help your child write the labels on the diagram.

Little Red Hen • **Book 1.2/Unit 2**   57

Name _____

Say the name of the picture.
Listen to the vowel sounds in **Ben** and **Bob**.

**Write the letter e or o to complete each word.
Then circle the picture the word names.**

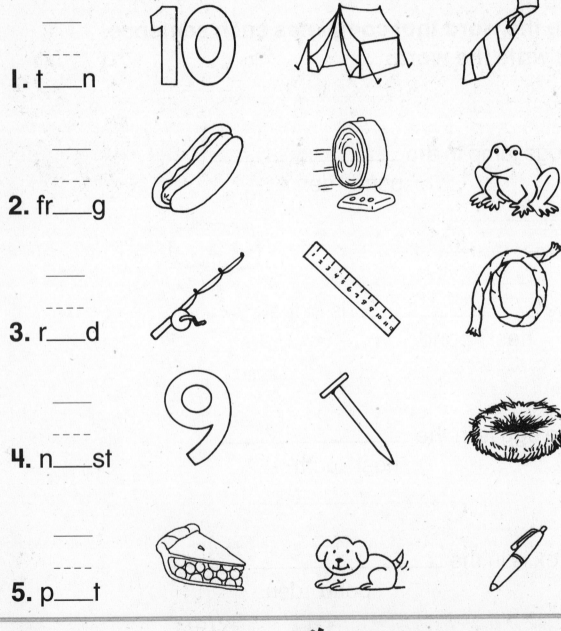

1. t___n

2. fr___g

3. r___d

4. n___st

5. p___t

At Home: Have your child write two words that have the
same vowel sound as Ben. Do the same with Bob.

Say each word. Listen to the beginning sound.

shin   **th**in

Say each word. Listen to the ending sound.

wi**sh**   wi**th**

Name each picture. Write the letters <u>th</u> or <u>sh</u> on the line.

1. fi_____

2. _____ip

3. th_____

4. ba_____

Write a sentence using a word from above.

_____

_____

_____

_____

 At Home: With your child, think of words that begin or end with *sh* and *th*.

Use a word from the box to complete each sentence.

live	into	out	Many

_____
- - - - - - - - -

1. Clams _____ in a shell.

_____
- - - - - - - - -

2. _____ ants live in the grass.

_____
- - - - - - - - -

3. The fox looks _____ of its den.

_____
- - - - - - - - -

4. The pigs went _____ the pen.

Draw a picture to show where you live.

At Home: Have your child think of another sentence using one of the words in the box.

© Macmillan/McGraw-Hill

Name _____

**As you read <u>A Prairie Dog Home</u>, fill in the
Main Idea and Details Web.**

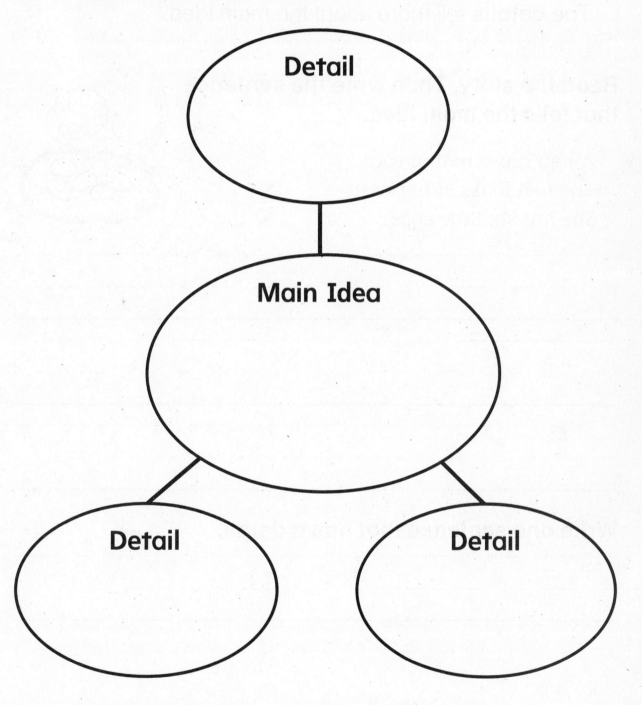

**How does the Main Idea and Details Web help you
better understand <u>A Prairie Dog Home</u>?**

© Macmillan/McGraw-Hill

 At Home: Have your child use the web to retell the story.

Name _____

> The **main idea** tells what the story is about.
>
> The **details** tell more about the main idea.

Read the story. Then write the sentence that tells the main idea.

A hen has a nest of eggs.
The hen looks at her nest.
She has six little eggs.

_____

- -

_____

- -

_____

- -

_____

Write one sentence that has a detail.

_____

- -

_____

© Macmillan/McGraw-Hill

 At Home: Talk with your child about a favorite story or TV show. Talk about the main idea and two important details from the story or show.

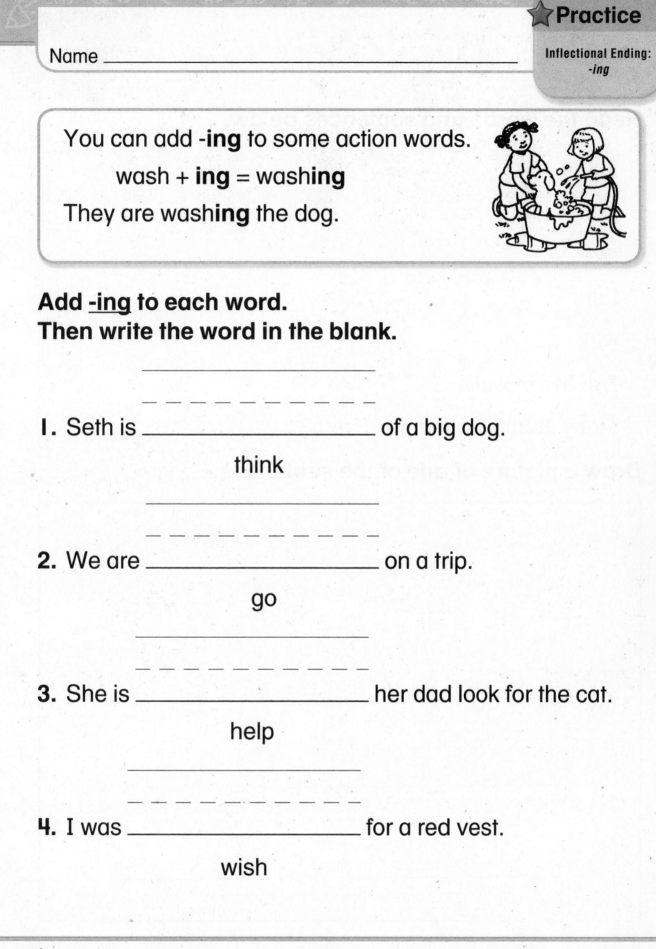

You can add **-ing** to some action words.

wash + **ing** = wash**ing**

They are wash**ing** the dog.

Add -ing to each word.
Then write the word in the blank.

_____

1. Seth is _____ of a big dog.

think

_____

2. We are _____ on a trip.

go

_____

3. She is _____ her dad look for the cat.

help

_____

4. I was _____ for a red vest.

wish

At Home: Have your child write a sentence using another
word with *-ing*.

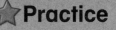

Read the words and sentences below.

many

fish

live

thin

with

Fish live in water.

Many animals live in the forest.

Draw a picture of one of the sentences.

 At Home: Help your child read the words and sentences above.

Name _____

A **dictionary** gives the meaning of words.

hop   to jump on one

ship   a big

wash   to use SOAP   and

Write the word that completes each sentence. You can use a word more than once.

_____
- - - - - - - - - -

1. She will go on a trip on a big _____.

_____
- - - - - - - - - -

2. I like to jump and _____.

_____
- - - - - - - - -

3. Dan helps _____ the dog.

_____
- - - - - - - - -

4. He can _____ on one leg.

At Home: Look up these words in the dictionary with your
child. Read the meanings and example sentences. Ask your
child to use one word in a sentence of his or her own.

A Prairie Dog Home • **Book 1.2/Unit 2**   65

© Macmillan/McGraw-Hill

Name _____

Say each word. Listen to the ending sound.

wi**sh**   wi**th**

Say each word. Listen to the beginning sound.

shin   **th**in

Say each word. Listen to the middle sound.

th**e**n   sh**o**p

Write the letters th, sh, e, or o to complete each picture name.

1. w_____ll

2. B_____th

3. _____ip

4. bru_____

5. _____ink

6. pa_____

 At Home: With your child make up sentences using words
that begin and end with *sh* and *th* and words with the short *o*
and *e* sounds.

© Macmillan/McGraw-Hill

Name _____

Look at the picture. The letter **u** stands for the middle sound in **bug** and **rug**.

b**u**g   r**u**g

Write the letter u̲ to complete the words. Draw a line from each picture to its name.

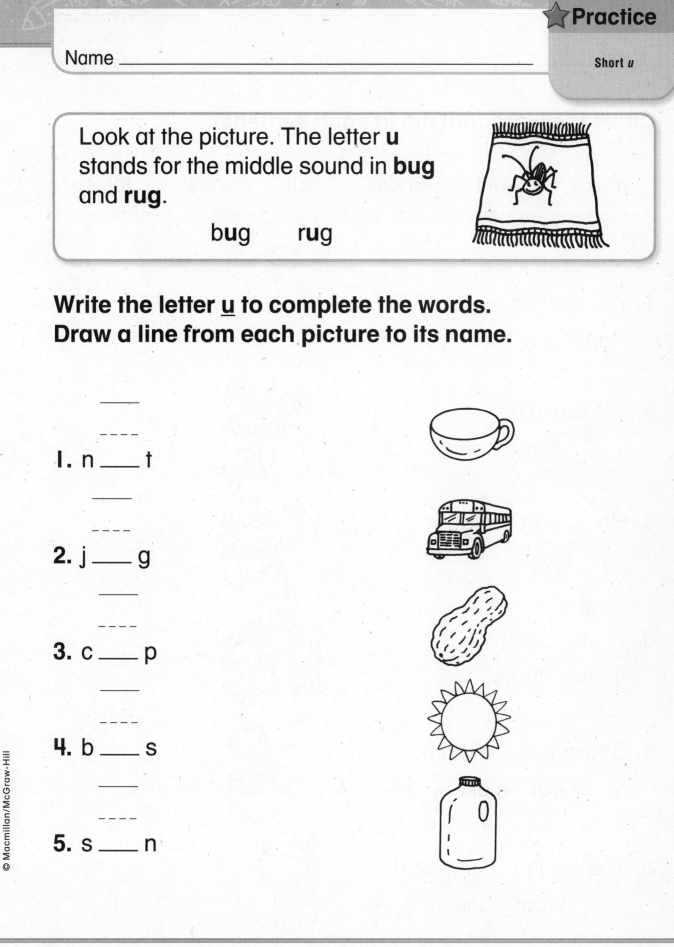

1. n ___ t

2. j ___ g

3. c ___ p

4. b ___ s

5. s ___ n

At Home: Have your child write another word that has the same vowel sound as *bug*.

Name _____

Circle the word that fits in each sentence.

make	want	under	put	show	three

1. I ___ to run.

   want   put

2. We are in a ___.

   three   show

3. He ___ on a cap.

   put   make

4. I see ___ cats.

   under   three

5. She can ___ a drum.

   put   make

6. The cat is ___ the bed.

   want   under

© Macmillan/McGraw-Hill

 At Home: Have your child think of another sentence using one of the words in the box.

As you read <u>The Fun Kids' Band</u>, fill in the Retelling Chart.

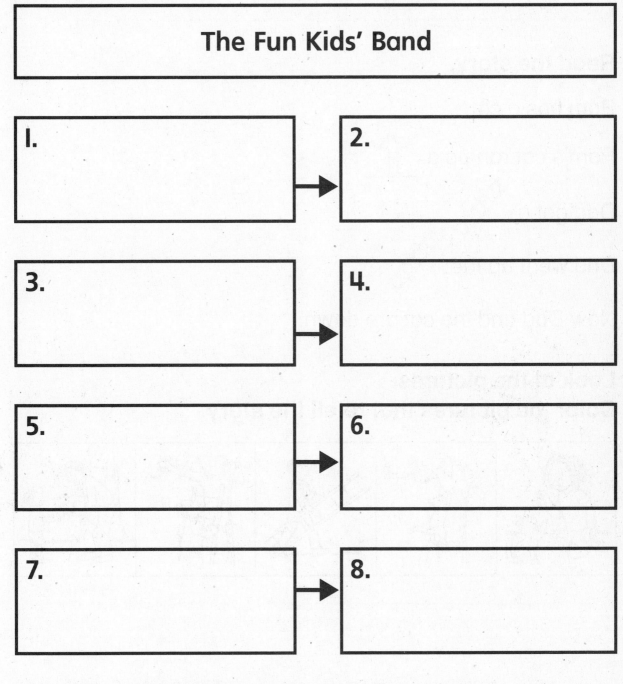

The Fun Kids' Band

1.

2.

3.

4.

5.

6.

7.

8.

How does the Retelling Chart help you visualize what happens in <u>The Fun Kids' Band</u>?

© Macmillan/McGraw-Hill

At Home: Have your child use the chart to retell the story.

Name _____

> When you **retell** a story, you tell it a shorter way.
> You tell only the important parts.

Read the story.

Pam has a cat.

Pam's cat ran up a  .

Dad got a .

Dad went up the .

Now Dad and the cat are down.

Look at the pictures.
Color the pictures that retell the story.

 At Home: Read or tell your child a simple story. Talk about the most important parts of the story. Ask your child to retell the story using his or her own words.

Name _____

A **contraction** is a short form of two words. One or more letters are replaced by an **apostrophe** (').

he + is = **he's**

Draw a line from the words to the contraction.

1. what is   she's

2. that is   let's

3. let us   what's

4. she is   it's

5. it is   that's

Add the apostrophe (') to the contraction.

6. do + not = dont

7. can + not = cant

8. he + is = hes

 At Home: Ask your child to make up a sentence with one of the contractions above.

Read the words and sentences below.

put
bug
rug
fun
under

That show was fun.
A bug is under the rug.

Draw a picture of one of the sentences.

 At Home: Help your child read the words and sentences above.

Name _____

Directions are the steps that you follow to make
or do something.

Read the directions.

Make a Print

1. Cut.   2. Dip.   3. Press.

Write 1, 2, and 3 to show the steps.

_____   _____   _____

At Home: Have your child think of directions to do or make
something. Write the steps in order. Help your child read
and follow them.

The Fun Kids' Band • Book 1.2/Unit 2

Say the name of the picture. The letter **u** stands for the middle sound in **bus**.

b**u**s

Name the pictures. Write <u>a</u>, <u>e</u>, <u>i</u>, <u>o</u>, or <u>u</u> to complete the words

1.

m ___ p

2.

s ___ n

3.

b ___ d

4.

c ___ t

5.

p ___ g

6.

t ___ b

 At Home: Have your child write a word that has the same vowel sound as each of these words: *cat, bed, pig, mop, tub.*

 The letters **cl** stand for the sounds at the beginning of **clock**.

Write the letters bl, cl, or fl to complete the words.

Draw a line from each picture to the matching word.

1. _____ip

2. _____ock

3. _____ag

4. _____ack

5. _____ap

Name _____

Circle the word that completes each sentence. Write the word on the line

_____

1. You will have to put the 👢 _____.

              today   away   school

_____

2. If the bus does not come, I will be _____.

            late   away   why

_____

3. We go this _____ to school.

    away   today   way

_____

4. We had 🍦 _____.

    away   school   today

_____

5. _____ did the bus go in the mud?

Late   Why   Way

_____

6. On 📅 I do not go to _____.

    today   late   school

At Home: Ask your child to make up a sentence using two of the answers above.

Name _____

As you read <u>On My Way to School</u>, fill in the Sequence Chart.

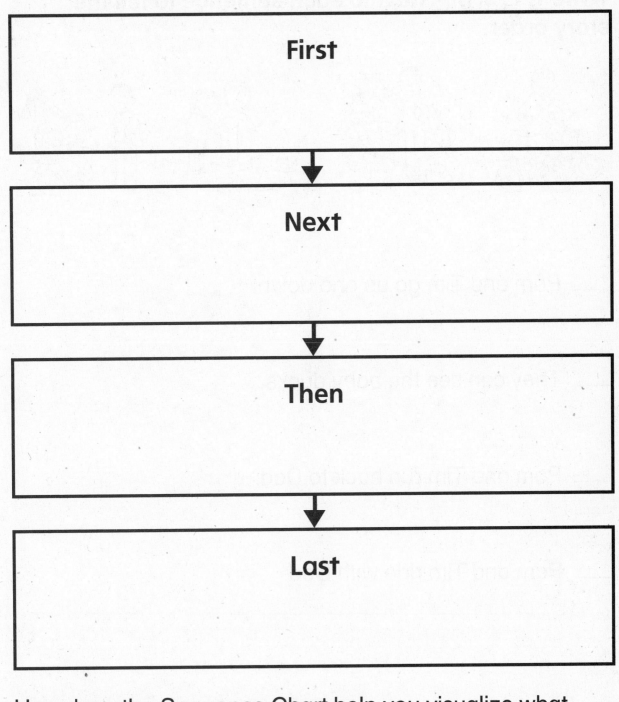

First

↓

Next

↓

Then

↓

Last

How does the Sequence Chart help you visualize what happens in <u>On My Way to School</u>?

 At Home: Have your child use the chart to retell the story.

Name _____

Look at the pictures.
Read the sentences.
Write 1, 2, 3, or 4 next to each sentence to tell the
story order.

_____

_____ Pam and Tim go up and down.

_____ They can see the baby ducks.

_____ Pam and Tim run back to Dad.

_____ Pam and Tim ride with Dad.

 At Home: Have your child describe in order what is
happening in each picture.

Name _____

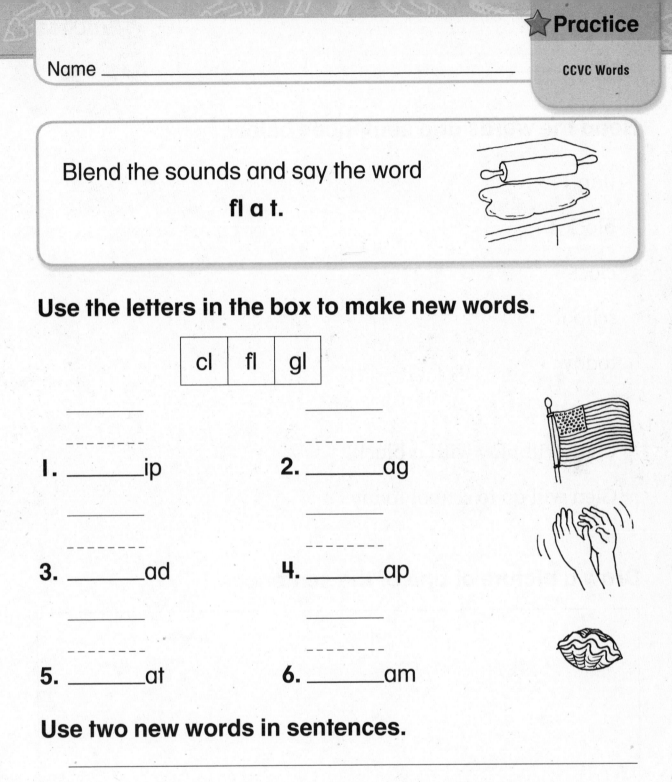

Blend the sounds and say the word
fl a t.

Use the letters in the box to make new words.

cl	fl	gl

1. _____ip

2. _____ag

3. _____ad

4. _____ap

5. _____at

6. _____am

Use two new words in sentences.

7. _____

8. _____

 At Home: Ask your child to write another word with the CCVC pattern, and draw a picture of it.

On My Way to School
Book 1.2/Unit 2

 79

© Macmillan/McGraw-Hill

Name _____

Read the words and sentences below.

flag

block

clock

school

today

Clem will play with a block.

Glen will go to school today.

Draw a picture of one of the sentences.

 At Home: Help your child read the words and sentence above.

Name _____

A **sign** uses words or pictures to tell you what to do.

Circle the word that completes each sentence. Then write the word.

1. The [STOP] tells you to _____.

   stop   go

2. The [sign] tells you where you can _____.

   play   fish

3. The [sign] tells you not to _____ here.

   fish   play

4. The [sign] tells you where the _____ is.

   show   school

© Macmillan/McGraw-Hill

At Home: Talk about other signs that you and your child might have seen at school or on the way to school. Have your child draw a picture of one of the signs.

On My Way to School
Book 1.2/Unit 2

81

Read each word. Draw a line from the word to the matching picture.

1. clip

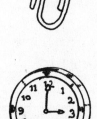

2. clap

3. block

4. black

5. flag

6. clock

 At Home: Ask your child to draw a picture of another word that begins with *cl*, *fl*, or *bl*. Then write the word next to it.

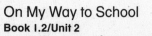

© Macmillan/McGraw-Hill

Name _____

Circle the word that completes the sentence.

1.

The cat is ___ the bed.
under   on

2.

Ned will go ___.
in   out

3.

This is ___ hot pot.
cup   one

4.

The pet will ___.
eat   run

5.

He will go ___.
away   fun

6.

___ jump and play.
She   They

Circle the words that tell about the pictures.

1.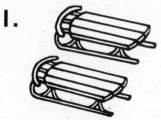

two sleds

one sled

2.

sun out

some nuts

3.

two pots

many pens

4.

two cats

three pups

5.

her school

big ship

6.

make a mess

clap hands

Name _____

Say the word. Listen to the **long a** sound.
The letters **a** and **e** stand for the **long a** sound.

cake

Write the letters <u>a</u> and <u>e</u> on the lines. Circle the picture to match the word you made.

1. r ___ k ___

2. g ___ t ___

3. l ___ k ___

4. g ___ m ___

5. c ___ n ___

© Macmillan/McGraw-Hill

At Home: Write the long *a* words on a sheet of paper. Have
your child underline the *a* and *e*, then read the words.

Kate's Game • **Book 1.3/Unit 3**

 85

Name _____

Circle the word that completes each sentence.
Write the word on the line.

_____

1. I said _____ to Jim.   hello   hat

2. _____ you get the bat?   Come   Could

3. Nan can _____ the box.   pull   hop

4. Tom can _____ fast.   went   walk

5. _____, yes. I can help.   Go   Oh

6. Can I have _____ the gum?   all   and

 At Home: Read the words in the box with your child. Have your child make up a sentence using two of the words.

Name _____

As you read <u>Kate's Game</u>, fill in the Predictions Chart.

What I Predict	What Happens

How does the Predictions Chart help you understand what happens in <u>Kate's Game</u>?

At Home: Have your child use the chart to retell the story.

Kate's Game • **Book 1.3/Unit 3** ⭐ **87**

© Macmillan/McGraw-Hill

Name _____

A **prediction** tells what might happen next.

What is next?

prediction

Draw a line under the correct picture.

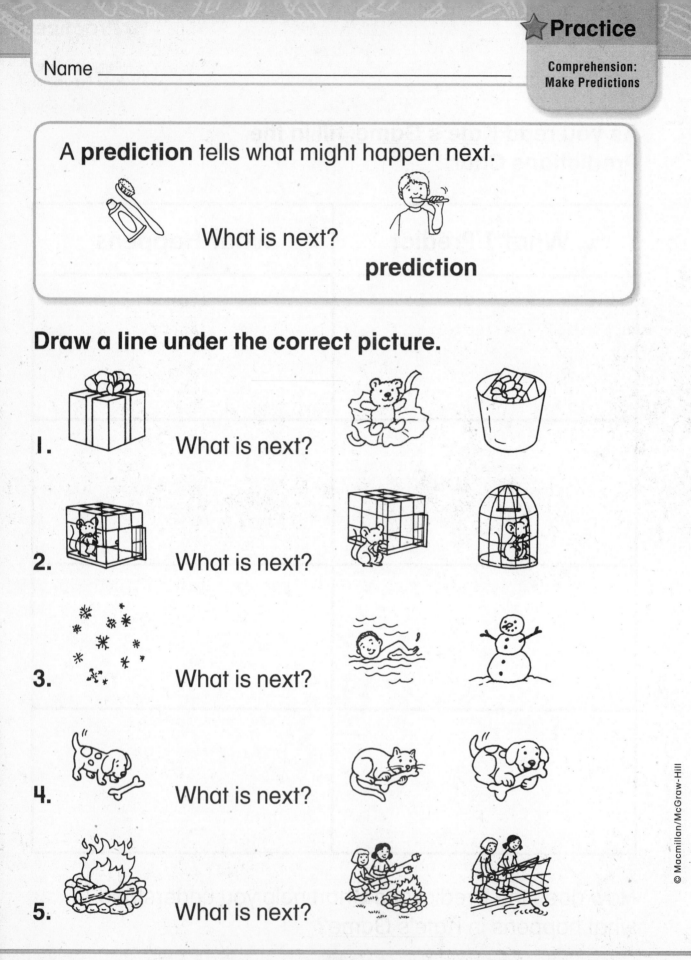

1. What is next?

2. What is next?

3. What is next?

4. What is next?

5. What is next?

 At Home: Read a story with your child. Stop at the bottom of each page. Ask your child to predict what will happen next.

Name _____

Look at the word: **bake**

Notice that the **e** is dropped when adding **-ed** and **-ing**.

bak**e** + **ed** = bak**ed**

bak**e** + **ing** = bak**ing**

Add -ed or -ing to the words below. Remember to drop the final e.

1. rake + ed = _____

2. rake + ing = _____

3. tape + ed = _____

4. tape + ing = _____

5. wade + ed = _____

6. wade + ing = _____

At Home: Have your child read the above words that have inflectional endings.

Kate's Game • Book 1.3/Unit 3

89

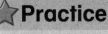
Name _____

Read the words and sentences below.

came

game

take

make

walk

He came over to play.

We will play a fun game.

We will take a walk too.

Draw a picture of one of the sentences.

© Macmillan/McGraw-Hill

At Home: Help your child read the words and
sentences above.

Name _____

A **map** can show where streets are. Some maps have **labels** that tell where places are. Look at the street map below.

The vet is on **Lake St**.

Look at the map. Fill in the blanks.

Lake St.   Plum St.   Vet   Red St.

Bond St   H   ⚬ ◯ ⌇

School

1. The ⚬ ◯ ⌇ is on _____.

2. The 📖 is on _____.

3. The school is on _____.

4. The 📫 is on _____.

5. The H is on _____.

At Home: Draw lines on a large sheet of paper to make a street map. Have your child cut out magazine pictures to glue on the map. Take turns giving clues to find places.

Kate's Game • **Book 1.3/Unit 3**

Name _____

Circle the word that names the picture.

1. van   vane

2. can   cane

3. rat   rate

4. cap   cape

5. tap   tape

6. pan   pane

7. mane   man

8. lan   lane

At Home: Read the words on the page. Help your child decide if the word has the *long a* or *short a* sound.

Name _____

Sometimes two consonants form a **blend**. You can hear each consonant sound in a **consonant blend**. Listen to the blends at the beginning of the word.

sled

Circle the letters that stand for the sound you hear at the beginning of each picture name.

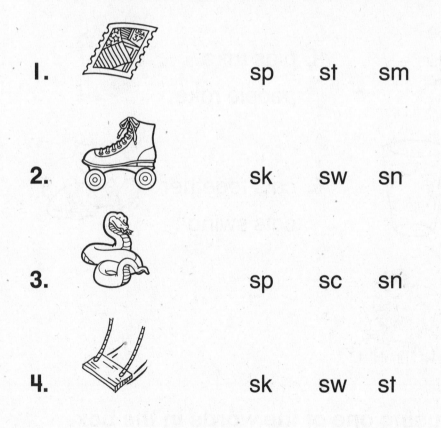

1.   sp   st   sm

2.   sk   sw   sn

3.   sp   sc   sn

4.   sk   sw   st

 At Home: Fold a piece of paper in half. Write *st* on one side and *sn* on the other. Look for magazine pictures to match each beginning sound.

Name _____

| boy | when | people | water |
| care | girl | together | |

Circle the words that tell about the picture.

1. boy runs
   bugs run

2. gate jump
   girl jumps

3. when
   where

4. pigs rake
   people rake

5. glass of water
   glass of mud

6. cats together
   cats swing

7. came to baby
   care for baby

Write a sentence using one of the words in the box.

_____

- -

_____

At Home: Write "People work together." on a piece of paper.
Help your child read the sentence. Then have your child
draw pictures of people working together.

© Macmillan/McGraw-Hill

As you read <u>Kids Can Help</u>, fill in the Compare and Contrast Chart.

Job	Kids in One Place	Kids in Another Place

How does the Compare and Contrast Chart help you better understand <u>Kids Can Help</u>?

At Home: Have your child use the chart to retell the story.

© Macmillan/McGraw-Hill

When you **compare** two things, you see how they are **alike**.

When you **contrast** two things, you see how they are **different**.

Color the picture pairs that are alike.

Circle the picture pairs that are different.

1.

2.

3.

4.

5.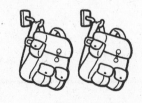

6.

 At Home: Select two articles of clothing. Have your child compare and contrast the clothes.

A **syllable** is a part of a word.
You can count the number of syllables in a word by
counting the number of beats in the word.

dis•play = 2   top = 1

Circle the number of syllables in each word.

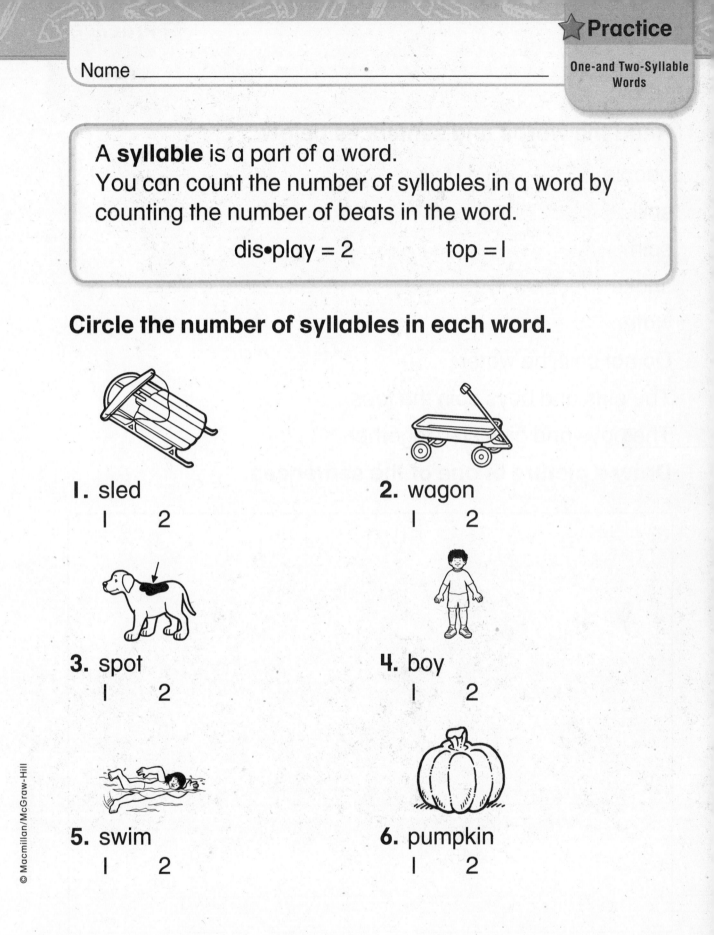

1. sled

1   2

2. wagon

1   2

3. spot

1   2

4. boy

1   2

5. swim

1   2

6. pumpkin

1   2

At Home: Say the names of your family members.
Count the syllables in each name.

Kids Can Help • **Book 1.3/Unit 3**

Read the words and sentences below.

people

spill

spin

snake

water

Do not spill the water.

The girls and boys spin the tops.

The boys and girls sled together.

Draw a picture of one of the sentences.

At Home: Help your child read the words and sentences above.

Name _____

Writers choose interesting and colorful words when they write poems.

See the **soft red** .

Match the descriptive words to the pictures.

1. two, small

2. red, fast

3. soft, little

4. one, black

5. three, big

6. hot, wet

At Home: Choose an object such as an intricate toy. Have your child think of as many words as possible to describe the object.

Kids Can Help • **Book 1.3/Unit 3**   99

Name _____

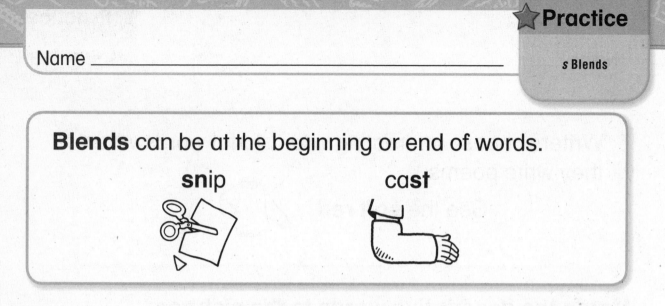

Blends can be at the beginning or end of words.

snip   ca**st**

Use a blend to name each picture.

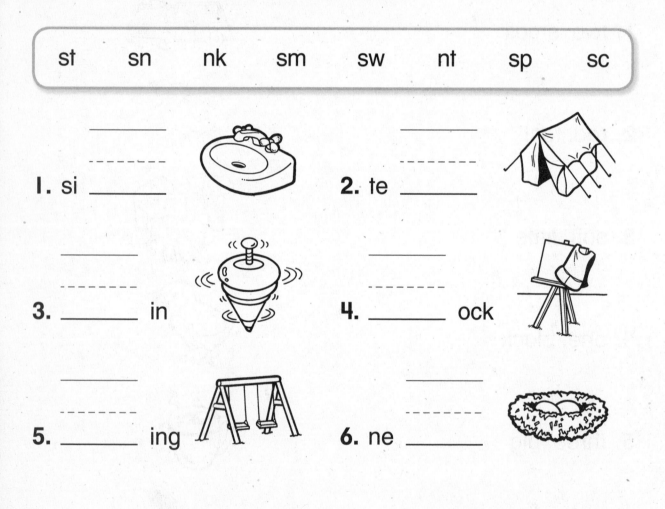

| st | sn | nk | sm | sw | nt | sp | sc |

1. si _____

2. te _____

3. _____ in

4. _____ ock

5. _____ ing

6. ne _____

At Home: Write *stop, snip, rink, went, spot,* and *disc* on a piece of paper. Help your child read the words. Then have your child circle all the blends.

© Macmillan/McGraw-Hill

Name _____

The letters **ch** and **tch** stand for the sound you hear in **ch**op and fe**tch**.

The letters **wh** stand for the sound you hear in **wh**ale.

Circle the word that describes each picture. Then write the word on the line.

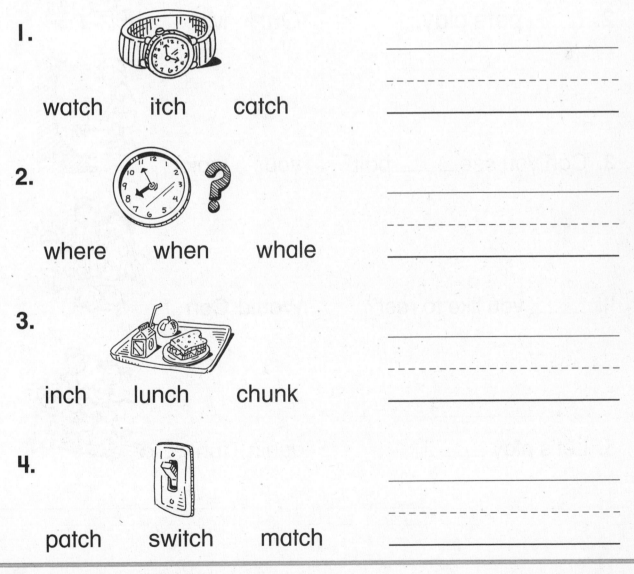

1.
watch   itch   catch

2.
where   when   whale

3.
inch   lunch   chunk

4.
patch   switch   match

 At Home: Help your child to use one of the circled words to write a sentence about day or night.

Short Shadows, Long Shadows
Book 1.3/Unit 3

 101

© Macmillan/McGraw-Hill

Name _____

Circle the word that completes each sentence.

1. In the day, it is _____ out.   light   little

2. _____ pets play.   Our   Me

3. Can you see _____ ball?   your   look

4. _____ you like to rest?   Would Can

5. Let's play _____!   again fun

 At Home: Have your child tell about a favorite daytime activity using one or more of the circled words.

Name _____

**As you read Short Shadows, Long Shadows,
fill in the Main Idea and Details Web.**

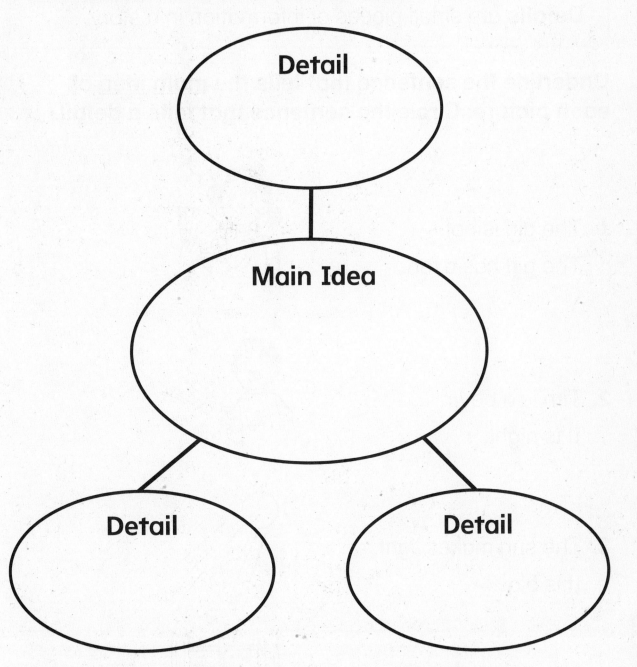

**How does the Main Idea and Details Web help you
better understand the main idea of Short Shadows,
Long Shadows?**

 At Home: Have your child use the chart to retell the story.

Short Shadows, Long Shadows
Book 1.3/Unit 3

The **main idea** tells the most important idea in a story.
Details are small pieces of information in a story.

Underline the sentence that tells the <u>main</u> <u>idea</u> of each picture. Circle the sentence that tells a <u>detail</u>.

1. The girl is hot.

The girl has a fan.

2. Tim is a boy.

It is night.

3. The sun makes light.

It is big.

4. The girl is asleep.

She sleeps with a bear.

 At Home: Ask your child to tell you about other details in each picture.

© Macmillan/McGraw-Hill

Name _____

Underline the word that completes each sentence.
Write the word on the line.

1. _____ can we do today?

     What   Why

2. Pat _____ the cat.

     fetches   watches

3. Ben _____ the cat.

     catches   munches

4. The day _____ fast!

     plays   passes

© Macmillan/McGraw-Hill

 At Home: Ask your child to make up a new sentence about
Ben and Pat, using a word that ends in -*es*.

Short Shadows, Long Shadows
Book 1.3/Unit 3

 105

Name _____

Read the words and sentences below.

catch

match

our

your

whale

Can you catch your shadow?

Our cat is small.

The whale is big.

Draw a picture of one of the sentences.

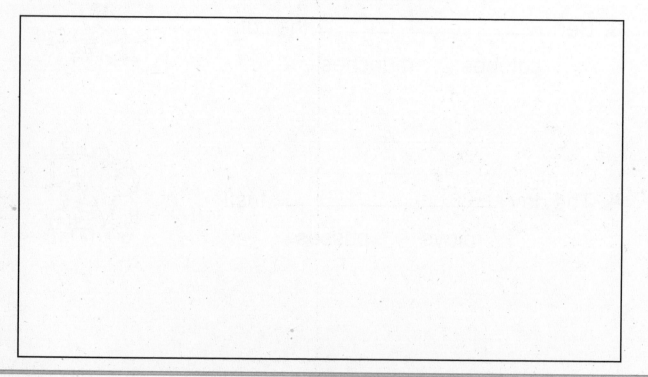

At Home: Help your child read the words and
sentences above.

The name of a magazine is its **title**.

Most magazines have **pictures** on the **cover**.

Circle <u>Yes</u> or <u>No</u> for each sentence.

1. The title of the magazine is <u>Fun in the Sun</u>.

   Yes   No

2. The cover has a picture.

   Yes   No

3. It is night in the picture.

   Yes   No

4. The magazine tells ways to play in the sun.

   Yes   No

 At Home: Ask your child to tell you what he or she might read about in the magazine.

Short Shadows, Long Shadows
Book 1.3/Unit 3
107

Name _____

Blend the sounds to read each word. Write the word. Then draw a line to the matching picture.

1. wh at

_____

- - - - - - - - - - - - - -

_____

2. p a tch

_____

- - - - - - - - - - - - - -

_____

3. i n ch

_____

- - - - - - - - - - - - - -

_____

4. ch a se

_____

- - - - - - - - - - - - - -

_____

5. c a tch

_____

- - - - - - - - - - - - - -

_____

© Macmillan/McGraw-Hill

 At Home: Ask your child to make up a silly sentence using at least two of the words on the page.

Name _____

Listen to the **long i** sound in **bike**
The letters **i** and **e** stand for the
long i sound.

bike

Write the letters i̱ and e̱ to complete each word. Draw a line from each picture to its name.

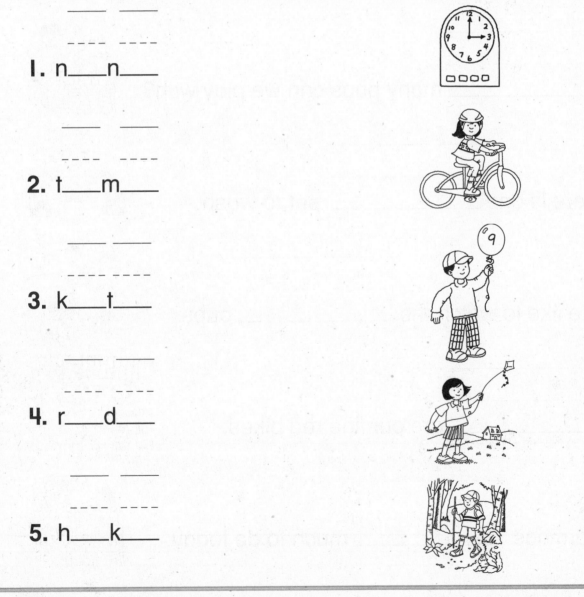

1. n___n___

2. t___m___

3. k___t___

4. r___d___

5. h___k___

 At Home: Have your child think of other words with the long *i* sound. Help your child write the words that follow the *i_e* pattern.

Smile, Mike! • **Book 1.3/Unit 3**   109

Name _____

Use the words in the box to complete the sentences.

| so | call | more | How | funny | There |

1. Now Mike will _____ his dog to him.

2. _____ many pups can we play with?

3. Here is one _____ pet to wash.

4. We like to watch the _____ pups.

5. _____ are our fine red bikes.

6. Sam has _____ much to do today.

At Home: Have your child create a sentence using one of the words in the box. Draw a picture to illustrate it.

As you read Smile, Mike!, fill in the Predictions Chart.

What I Predict	What Happens

How does the Predictions Chart help you understand what happens in Smile, Mike!?

At Home: Have your child use the chart to retell the story.

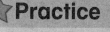
Look at the pictures. Predict what will happen next. Underline the answers to the questions.

1.

What will Kit and Pam do?   They will ride bikes.
They will sit down.

2.

What will Tim do?   Tim will run away.
Tim will help Mom.

3.

What will Dad and Kim
do now?   They will take the pup.
They will go away.

4.

What will Mike do now?   Mike will play on the slide.
Mike will go to bed.

© Macmillan/McGraw-Hill

At Home: Have your child use picture clues in a book you
read together to predict what will happen next.

When you add **-ing** or **-ed** to a word that ends with a vowel and a consonant, double the final consonant.

run + ing = ru**nn**ing   Sam is **running** down the hill.
sip + ed = si**pp**ed   Nan **sipped** the water.

**Change each word to complete the sentence.
Double the final consonant.**

_____
- - - - - - - - - - - - - - - - - - - -
1. Mike _____ on the ice on the pond.
   slip + ed =

_____
- - - - - - - - - - - - - - - - - - - -
2. We are _____ the ball game today.
   win + ing =

_____
- - - - - - - - - - - - - - - - - - - -
3. Sam likes _____ the three funny pups.
   pet + ing =

_____
- - - - - - - - - - - - - - - - - - - -
4. We _____ at the shop.
   stop + ed =

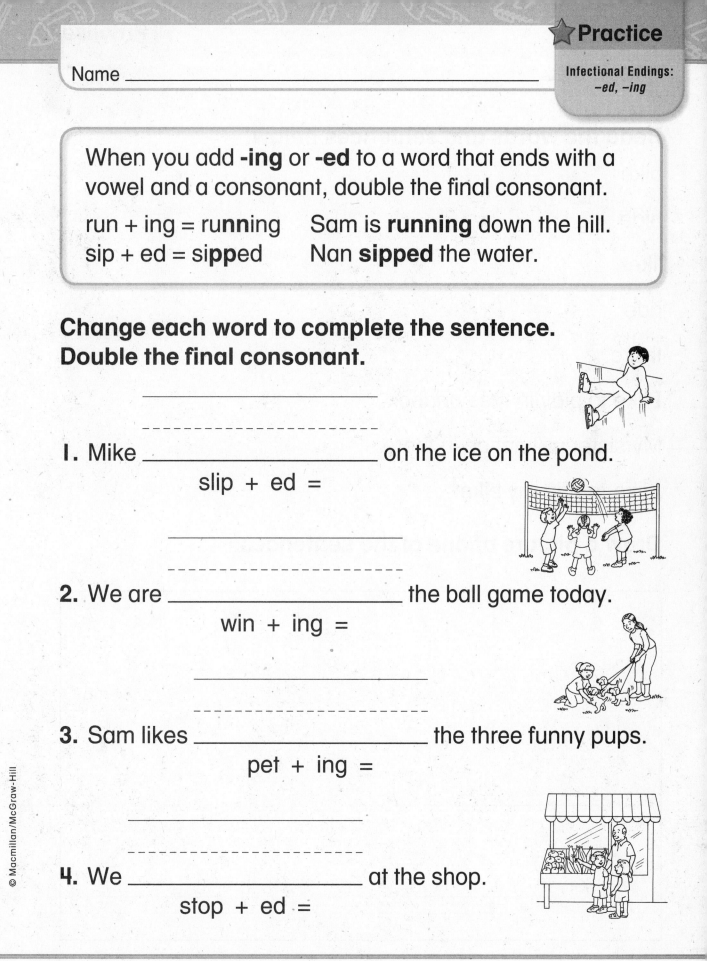

 At Home: Have your child write two more words that double the final consonant with the endings −ed and −ing.

Smile, Mike! • **Book 1.3/Unit 3**   **113**

Read the words and sentences below.

bike

hide

like

ride

there

I like to play in the sandbox.

My sister will not go in there.

I like to ride my bike.

Draw a picture of one of the sentences.

 At Home: Help your child read the words and sentences above.

Name _____

Read this chart.

Mike's Pets
cats II
ferret I
fish ᚻᚻ ᚻᚻ
mice III

Kim's Pets
cats III
dogs II
fish ᚻᚻ IIII
mice ᚻᚻ I

Circle the correct answer.

1. How many cats does Mike have?

two   three

2. How many dogs does Kim have?

one   two

3. How many mice does Mike have?

six   three

4. How many fish does Kim have?

nine   five

5. Mike has a kind of pet that Kim doesn't have. What is it?

fish   ferret

At Home: Have your child answer one more question about the chart.

115

Name _____

Say the word. Listen to the **long i**
sound that the letters **i** and **e** stand for.

k**ite**

Listen to the **short i** sound that the
letter **i** stands for.

s**i**t

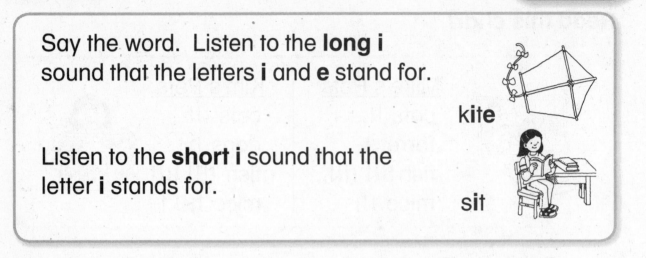

**Circle the letters that stand for the long i or short i
sound. Match each word to its picture.**

1. bike

2. hill

3. mitt

4. smile

5. ride

 At Home: Have your child make up sentences for one of the
i_e and the *i* words above.

Name _____

Three consonants can form a blend. You can hear each consonant sound in a blend.

s c r= scr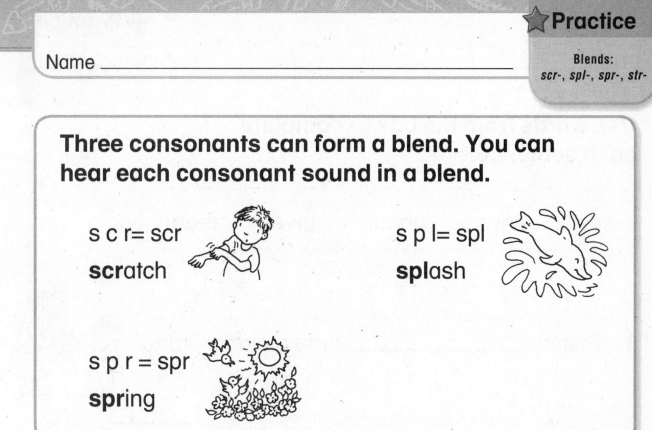
scratch

s p l= spl
splash

s p r = spr
spring

Circle the word that completes the sentence.

1. The ducks like to _____ in the water.

      splash   splint

2. The cat is _____.

    spring   striped

3. This girl has a _____.

    scratch   scruff

4. I like to play outside in the _____.

    scrape   spring

© Macmillan/McGraw-Hill

 At Home: Have your child draw a picture of spring and label it "spring."

Name _____

Use words from the box to complete each sentence.

say	says	about	give	read

1. "Please _____ me a plum, Gram."

   _____

2. This is a book _____ cats.

   _____

3. "I want to _____ this book."

   _____

4. "Please read it to me," I _____.

   _____

5. "Let's read it together," Gram _____.

 At Home: Help your child use one of the words from the box in a sentence.

Name _____

As you read Gram and Me, fill in the Character and Setting Chart.

Setting	What the Characters Do There
1.	1.
2.	2.
3.	3.
4.	4.

How does the Character and Setting Chart help you retell Gram and Me?

At Home: Have your child use the chart to retell the story.

A **character** is a person or animal in a story.
The **setting** of a story is where it takes place.

Look at the picture. Color the characters.

Circle the words that tell about the setting.
Underline the words that tell about the characters.

sand	boy	swing
kids	slide	girl

 At Home: Have your child draw a new setting for the characters above.

Name _____

Contractions combine two words.

The apostrophe (') takes the place of the missing letter or letters.

we + will = **we'll**   I + am = **I'm**   you + have = **you've**

**Circle the contraction in each sentence.
Underline the words that make the contraction.**

I. I've made this with strips of string.

You have   I have

2. We'll buy this striped shirt.

We will   You have

3. I'm going to school.

I am   You have

4. You've got an itch to scratch!

We will   You have

© Macmillan/McGraw-Hill

 At Home: Have your child choose one of the words he or she circled and use it in a sentence.

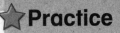
Name _____

Read the words and sentences below.

scrub

string

says

were

splash

She says many funny things.

My cat Stripes plays with string.

The duck made a big splash.

Draw a picture of one of the sentences.

© Macmillan/McGraw-Hill

At Home: Help your child read the words and sentences above.

Name _____

A **numerical list** is a series of things written in **1,2,3** order.

Read the list of activities.

1. Ride a bike

2. Read a book

3. Play chess

Make a list of your favorite things to do. Use the activities above or add others. Number your list.

My favorite things: _____

_____

_____

© Macmillan/McGraw-Hill

 At Home: Have your child make a list of his or her three
favorite breakfast foods, in order of favorite.

Gram and Me • **Book 1.3/Unit 3** **123**

Circle the word to match the picture.

1. stripe   string

2. stop   split

3. skip   skate

4. spin   spring

5. flag   flip

6. school   scratch

 At Home: Help your child read the words that were not circled.

Circle the sentence that tells about the picture.

1. We swim.

Let's walk.

2. What time is it?

The light is on.

3. Pull the gate.

He can ride.

4. She can call.

She runs a race.

5. The girls wave.

They like rice.

6. I like baths.

We read together.

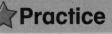
Name _____

Write the word that completes the sentence.

_____

- - - - - - - - - - - - - - - - -

1. _____ the pups like to ride.

Two   All

_____

- - - - - - - - - - - - - - - - -

2. _____ cat is little.

Our   When

_____

- - - - - - - - - - - - - - - - -

3. This is _____ I do it.

skate   how

_____

- - - - - - - - - - - - - - - - -

4. Kate and Jake _____ swimming.

were   can

_____

- - - - - - - - - - - - - - - - -

5. The _____ likes to ride.

bike   boy

© Macmillan/McGraw-Hill

Name _____

Read the word. Listen to the **long o** sound the letters **o** and **e** stand for.

bone

Circle the word that names the picture. Then write the word.

1. rode
   rose

   _____

   - - - - - - - - - - -

   _____

2. note
   not

   _____

   - - - - - - - - - - -

   _____

3. glob
   globe

   _____

   - - - - - - - - - - -

   _____

4. robe
   rope

   _____

   - - - - - - - - - - -

   _____

5. note
   nose

   _____

   - - - - - - - - - - -

   _____

6. home
   hose

   _____

   - - - - - - - - - - -

   _____

© Macmillan/McGraw-Hill

 At Home: Ask your child to make up a sentence for each of the words circled.

Pelican Was Hungry

Name _____

Circle the word that completes each sentence. Then write the word on the line.

1. I _____ a big duck.

saw
soon

2. The duck was _____ on the pond.

fixing
floating

3. The pond _____ in the sun.

sparkled
smelled

4. I did not see _____ other ducks.

saw
any

5. The duck _____ its bill.

only
opened

6. _____ the duck swam to its nest.

Some
Soon

7. I see the duck _____ day.

every
even

At Home: Have your child use two of the words circled to write a sentence about something he or she saw one day.

As you read <u>Pelican Was Hungry</u>, fill in the Inference Chart.

Text Clues	What You Know	Inferences

How does the Inference Chart help you better understand <u>Pelican Was Hungry</u>?

At Home: Have your child use the chart to retell the story.

Pelican Was Hungry
Book 1.4/Unit 4

129

© Macmillan/McGraw-Hill

Name _____

> You can use what you read and what you already know to help you better understand a story.

Look at the picture. Think about what you already know from looking at the picture. Then read the sentences. Circle the sentences that are true.

1. The wave is as tall as the man.

2. The water is red.

3. He has a shirt on.

4. He is sitting down.

5. The man knows how to surf.

Now write your own sentences about riding waves.

 At Home: Ask your child to explain the sentence he or she wrote.

© Macmillan/McGraw-Hill

Name _____

As I read, I will pay attention to the punctuation.

	Birds make nests in the spring.
6	Some birds make nests in trees.
12	Some birds make nests in bushes.
18	Some city birds make nests on buildings.
25	This is a robin. She makes her
32	nest in a tree. 36

Comprehension Check

1. When do birds make nests?

2. Where do birds make nests?

	Words Read	−	Number of Errors	=	Words Correct Score
First Read		−		=	
Second Read		−		=	

At Home: Help your child read the passage, paying attention to the goal at the top of the page.

Name _____

A **dictionary** is a book that gives the meaning of words. Some words have more than one meaning.

left 1. Your body has a **left** side and a right side: Pick up the pen with your **left** hand. **2. left** comes from the word leave: Grandfather **left** on time.

right 1. Your body has a **right** side and a left side: Can you put it in your **right** hand? **2. Right** also means not having a mistake: He got all his math **right**.

Match the word to all the pictures that show its meanings.

A.

1. left

B.

2. right

C.

D.

 At Home: Make up a silly sentence using the two meanings of the word *right*.

© Macmillan/McGraw-Hill

Name _____

Circle the word that completes each sentence. Then write the word.

1. A cat can run _____

than a duck.   faster   fastest

_____
- - - - - - - - - - - - - - - - - -

2. The big dog is the _____

dog on the block.   faster   fastest

_____
- - - - - - - - - - - - - - - - - -

3. That big bed is _____

than my bed.   softer   softest

_____
- - - - - - - - - - - - - - - - - -

4. I will take a nap on the

_____
- - - - - - - - - - - - - - - - - -
_____ bed.
softer   softest

At Home: Ask your child to make up another sentence for each of the words circled.

Poems often repeat words or sentences more than once.

Read the poem. Circle the sentences that repeat in the poem.

Pelican

The pelican is big.
Swim, fish, swim.

The pelican is fast.
Swim, fish, swim.

The pelican is hungry.
Swim, fish, swim.
GULP!

Write the words that are repeated.

_____

- -

_____

What do you think happens to the fish?

_____

- -

_____

© Macmillan/McGraw-Hill

 At Home: Have your child read the poem
aloud with expression.

Name _____

Read the words. The letters **o_e**, **i_e**, and **a_e** stand for the long vowel sound in **rope**, **five**, and **cake**.

rope 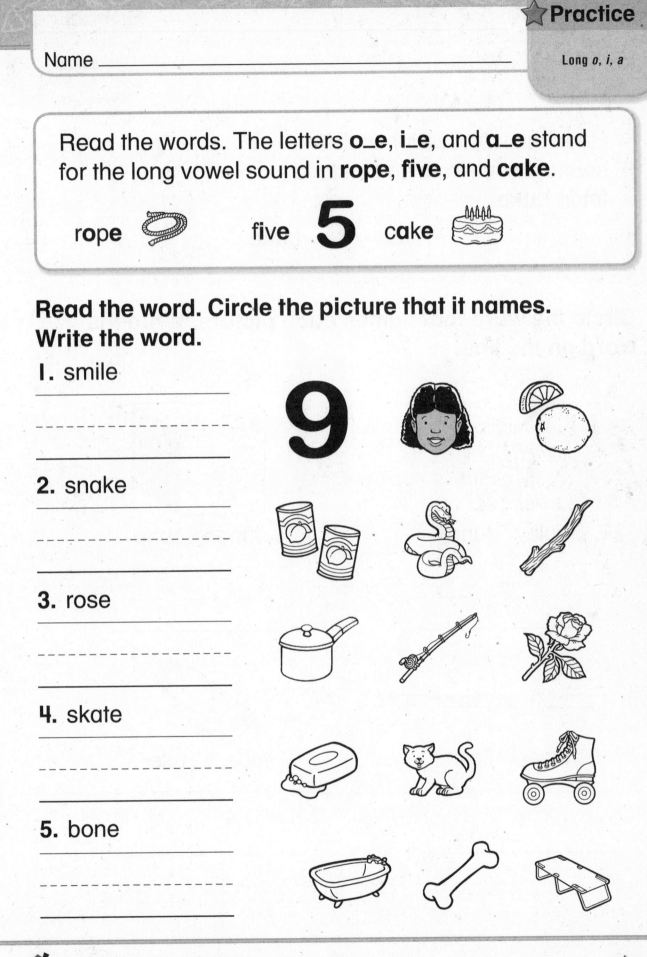 five **5** cake

Read the word. Circle the picture that it names. Write the word.

1. smile

2. snake

3. rose

4. skate

5. bone

At Home: Have your child look through catalogs or flyers to find long *o*, long *i*, and long *a* words.

Pelican Was Hungry
Book 1.4/Unit 4

135

© Macmillan/McGraw-Hill

Name _____

Read the word. Listen to the sound the letters **u** and **e** stand for in **Luke**.

Luke

Circle the word that names each picture. Write the word on the line.

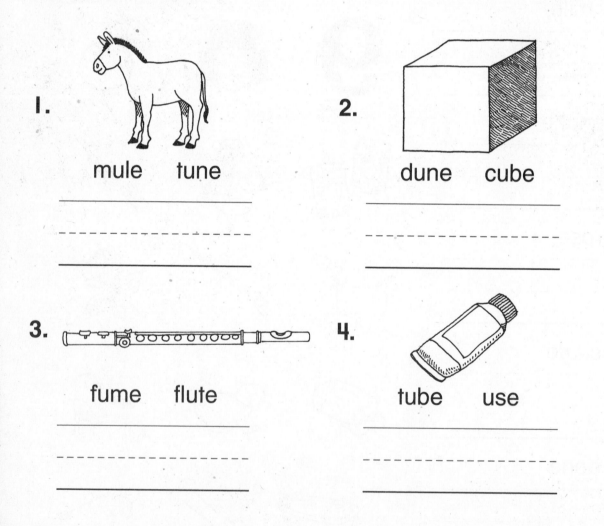

1.

mule   tune

_____
- - - - - - - - - - - - - -
_____

2.

dune   cube

_____
- - - - - - - - - - - - - -
_____

3.

fume   flute

_____
- - - - - - - - - - - - - -
_____

4.

tube   use

_____
- - - - - - - - - - - - - -
_____

 At Home: Have your child use one of the words he or she wrote above in a sentence.

© Macmillan/McGraw-Hill

Name _____

—Rags

Draw a line to the word that completes the sentence.

1. We _____ on a home for Rags.

find

2. I hope Rags likes his _____ home.

old

3. The _____ one fell down.

work

4. Can you _____ the saw?

new

5. We will be _____ soon.

creation

6. Rags likes our new _____.

after

7. We did a _____ job!

done

8. Rags will use his new home _____ his walk.

terrific

At Home: Have your child make up another sentence using one of the Words to Know.

As you read <u>June Robot Cleans Up</u>, fill in the Conclusion Chart.

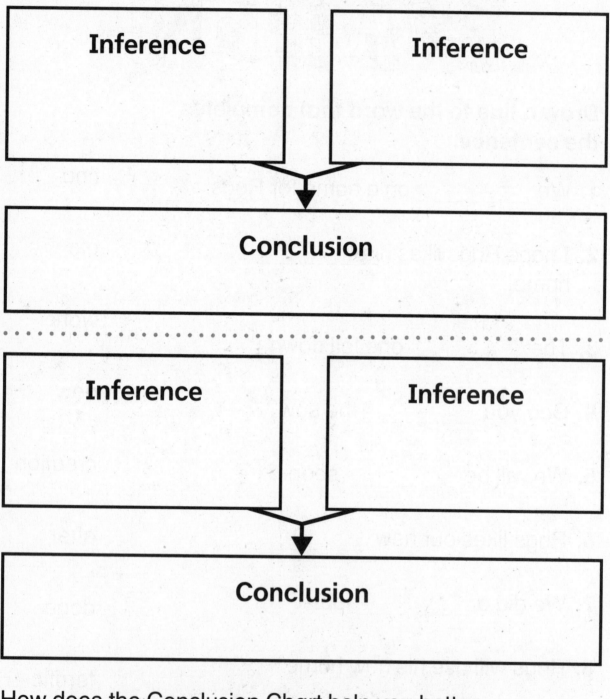

Inference	Inference

Conclusion

Inference	Inference

Conclusion

How does the Conclusion Chart help you better understand <u>June Robot Cleans Up</u>?

 At Home: Have your child use the chart to retell the story.

Name _____

You can use what you read and what you already know to help you **draw conclusions.**

Circle the picture that answers the question.

1. The pond is frozen. What can Luke do?

2. The girls have pet dogs. What can they do?

3. Jane is late. What can she do?

 At Home: Ask your child to draw conclusions about what to wear when it rains or snows. Have your child draw a picture of his or her conclusions.

June Robot Cleans Up
Book 1.4/Unit 4

 139

As I read, I will pay attention to the punctuation.

7	Find something old. You can use paper, a jug, or a can. Make something new
15	like a flowerpot!
18	Use what you find. Make a work of art
27	out of it. Show your creation to your
35	friends after you are done! 40

Comprehension Check

1. What could you make from old things?

2. What are some old things you can use in a new way?

© Macmillan/McGraw-Hill

	Words Read	–	Number of Errors	=	Words Correct Score
First Read		–		=	
Second Read		–		=	

 At Home: Help your child read the passage, paying attention to the goal at the top of the page.

Name _____

> **Context clues** are words in a sentence that help you figure out the meaning of a new word.

Use context clues to figure out the meaning of the word in bold letters.

Fill in the circle next to the correct answer.

1. The truck took the old tires to the **junkyard**.

   ○ a place for junk

   ○ a store that sells tables and chairs

2. The art teacher showed my **project** to the class.

   ○ backpack

   ○ something you do or make

3. Dan gave the **extra** pie to Ann after the party.

   ○ leftover

   ○ cute

4. As I walked along the **bank** of the river, I saw fish in the water.

   ○ the land next to a river

   ○ a small dog

At Home: Make up a sentence using one of the boldfaced words.

Name _____

Read the **CVCe** words. Listen for the long vowel sound.

cube   lace   ride

Write the word that answers the question.

1. Is this a cap or a cape?

_____

- - - - - - - - - - - - - - -

This is a _____.

2. Is this a bat or a bike?

_____

- - - - - - - - - - - - - - -

This is a _____.

3. Is this Pete or a pet?

_____

- - - - - - - - - - - - - - -

This is _____.

4. Is this a mule or mud?

_____

- - - - - - - - - - - - - - -

This is a _____.

Write a sentence using a <u>CVCe</u> word.

_____

- -

_____

At Home: Help your child find three CVCe words in a story book or magazine.

Name _____

A **floor plan** is a drawing that shows where things are in a room.

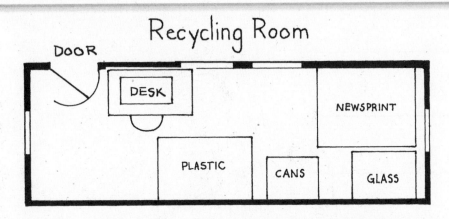

Recycling Room

Use the floor plan to answer the questions.

1. How many recycling bins do you see?

1   2   3   4

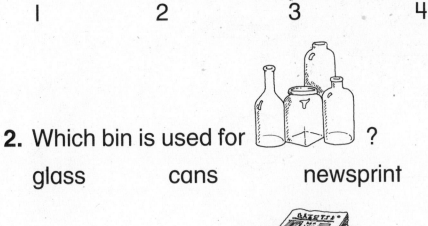

2. Which bin is used for  ?

glass   cans   newsprint

3. Which bin is used for  ?

plastic   cans   newsprint

4. Where can you ask for help?

plastic   desk   newsprint

 At Home: Have your child draw a floor plan of his or her bedroom. Help your child label his or her floor plan.

Use the words from the box to name each picture.

nose	tube	flute	hose	Luke	broke

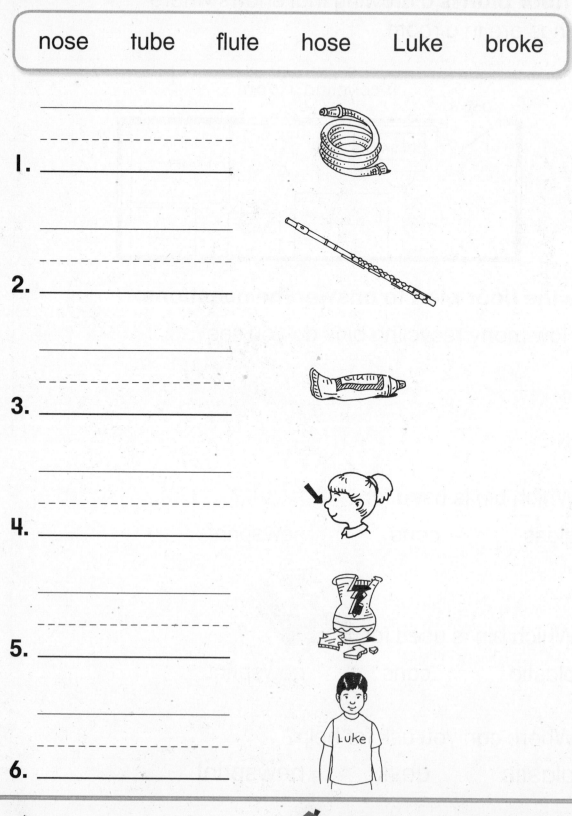

1. _____

2. _____

3. _____

4. _____

5. _____

6. _____

At Home: Have your child think of two words that have the same vowel sound as *Rose*. Do the same with *June*.

Read the words. The letters **ay** and **ai** stand for the **long a** sound.

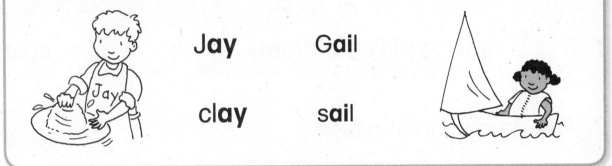

Jay   Gail

clay   sail

Circle the word that names each picture.
Write the word on the line.

1.

tray   play

_____

- - - - - - - - - - -

_____

2.

train   tail

_____

- - - - - - - - - - -

_____

3.

rain   raid

_____

- - - - - - - - - - -

_____

4.

bay   day

_____

- - - - - - - - - - -

_____

© Macmillan/McGraw-Hill

At Home: Ask your child to use each word in a sentence.

Name _____

Draw a line to the word that completes each sentence.

1. I _____ how to play the drums.   cold

2. The drums make a big _____.   know

3. The school play was _____!   their

4. Sam got a _____ hat from his
   grandma.   warm

5. It is much too _____ to swim.   predict

6. They went back to _____ homes
   after school.   sound

7. Did you _____ what he would say?   extreme

8. The cold was so _____ we all froze.   great

At Home: Have your child think of another sentence for one
of the Words to Know.

Name _____

© Macmillan/McGraw-Hill

As you read Stormy Weather, fill in the Compare and Contrast Chart.

Different → **Blizzard**

Alike →

Different → **Thunderstorm**

How does the Compare and Contrast Chart help you better understand Stormy Weather?

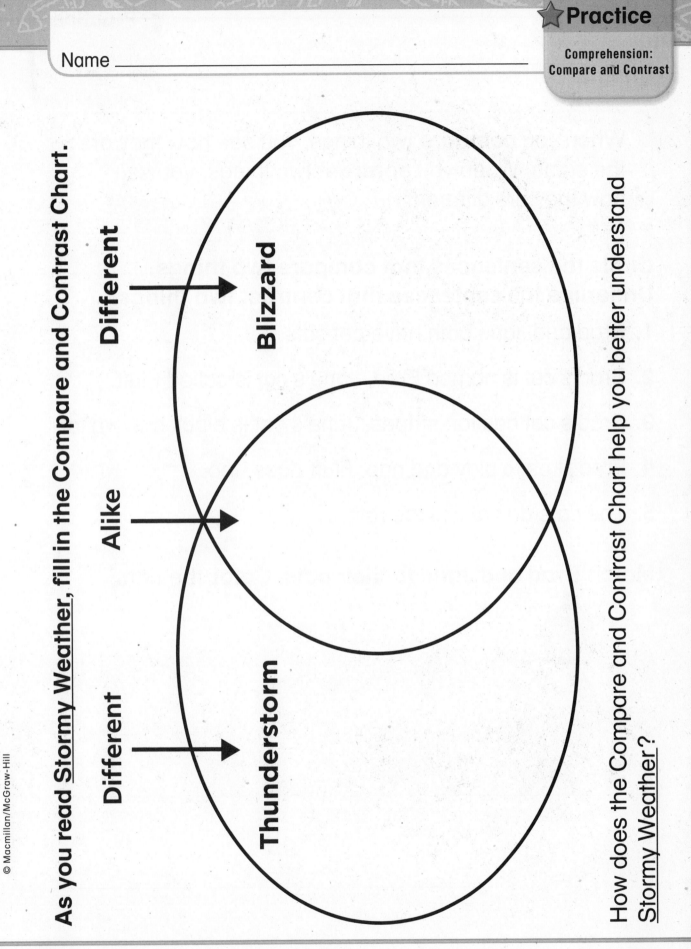

At Home: Have your child use the chart to retell the story.

Stormy Weather • **Book 1.4/Unit 4**

When you **compare** two things, you see how they are the same. When you **contrast** two things, you see how they are different.

Circle the sentences that compare two things.
Underline the sentences that contrast two things.

1. Brad and Jane both have pet cats.

2. Brad's cat is named Fred. Jane's cat is called Fluff.

3. Brad's cat has tan stripes. Jane's cat is black and white.

4. Fred likes to play and nap. Fluff does, too.

5. The cats do not like the rain.

Match Brad and Jane to their cats. Color the cats.

At Home: Ask your child to describe two people he or she knows. Have your child tell how they are alike and how they are different.

© Macmillan/McGraw-Hill

Name _____

Sometimes a **dictionary** has more than one meaning for a word.

Read the definitions below.

bat 1. a strong stick used to hit a baseball: Matt got a new baseball **bat**. 2. a small animal that has wings: A **bat** sleeps during the day.

letter 1. a part of the alphabet: C is the third **letter** in the alphabet. 2. a message that someone writes to someone else: My sister sent me a **letter**.

Use a word from the dictionary entries to complete each sentence.

1. I will write a _____ to my mom.

2. She will use a _____ to hit the ball.

3. A _____ has wings and lives in a cave.

4. What _____ is shaped like a snake?

At Home: Have your child think of another word with multiple meanings.

Stormy Weather • Book 1.4/Unit 4

149

© Macmillan/McGraw-Hill

As I read, I will pay attention to the punctuation.

	Do you see any clouds today?
6	Some clouds look like great white puffs.
13	Some clouds are gray.
17	You know it may rain when clouds are gray.
26	Is it raining?
29	You may see a flash in a cloud.
37	You know a great big sound will come next. 46

Comprehension Check

1. What might happen when clouds are gray?

2. What happens after you see a flash in a cloud?

	Words Read	–	Number of Errors	=	Words Correct Score
First Read		–		=	
Second Read		–		=	

© Macmillan/McGraw-Hill

At Home: Help your child read the passage, paying attention to the goal at the top of the page.

Name _____

> A **telephone directory** lists names, addresses,
> and telephone numbers.

Kail, James	14 Elm St.	555-5436
Kail, Jay	200 Main St.	555-7401
Kail, Laila	29 Sun Ave.	555-4269
Kail, Tom	9 Show Way	555-9711
Kal, May	17 Gray Ave.	555-5436

Use the directory to answer the questions.

1. How many people have the last name Kail?

4   5

2. Who has the last name Kal?

Jay   May

3. What is Laila Kail's phone number?

555-4269   555-7401

4. Where does Tom Kail live?

14 Elm St.   9 Show Way

5. Who lives on Main St.?

Jay   Laila

At Home: Help your child find a listing in the telephone
directory.

© Macmillan/McGraw-Hill

Name _____

> A **compound word** is made up of two small words.
>
> side + walk = **sidewalk**
> sun + set = **sunset**

Use the picture to answer the questions.

1. What is a **pack** you put on your **back**?

   _____

   -

   It is a _____.

2. What do you use to hit a **ball** and then run the **bases**?

   _____

   -

   You use a _____ bat.

3. What do you call the **sun** that is about to **set**?

   _____

   -

   It is a _____.

4. What **work** will the boys and girl do at **home**?

   _____

   -

   They will do their _____.

 At Home: Help your child find and read compound words in a newspaper or a catalog.

Read the words. Listen to the long vowel sound in each word.

Rose   Luke   Gail   Jay

Write the letters <u>o</u> or <u>u</u> and final <u>e</u> to complete the picture names.

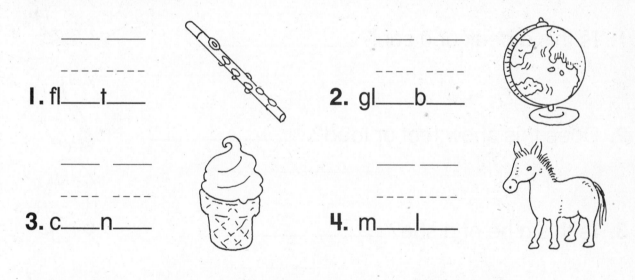

1. fl__t__

2. gl__b__

3. c__n__

4. m__l__

Write <u>ay</u> or <u>ai</u> to complete each picture name.

5. m____l

6. tr____

 At Home: Have your child think of other names that have long *u*, long *o*, or long *a* sound.

Stormy Weather • **Book 1.4/Unit 4**

★ 153

Listen to the sound the letters **ee**, **ea**, and **e** stand for in each word.

fee**t**   **m**e**at**   **w**e**

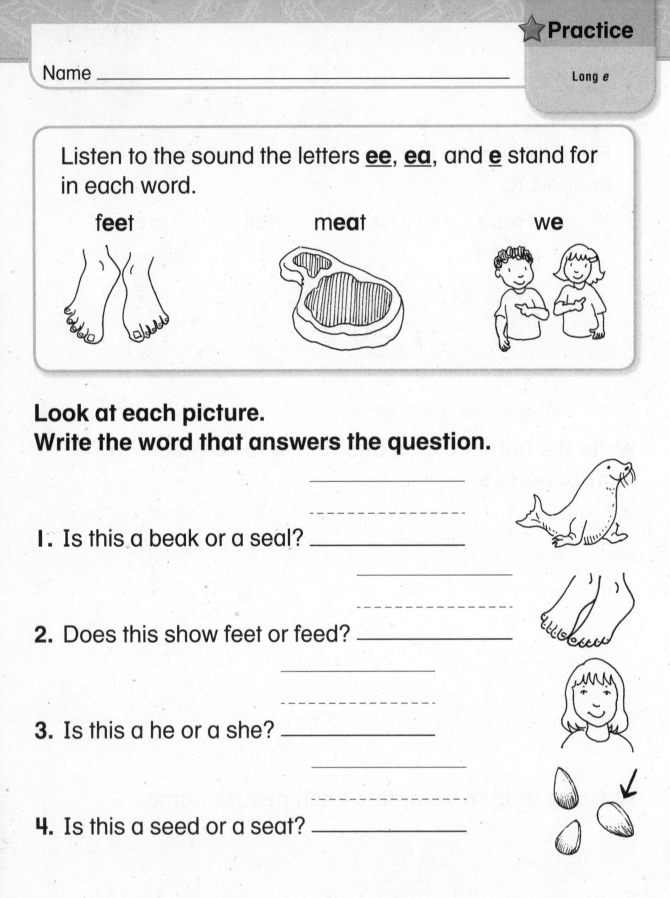

Look at each picture.
Write the word that answers the question.

_____
- - - - - - - - - - - - - - - - - -
1. Is this a beak or a seal? _____

_____
- - - - - - - - - - - - - - - - - -
2. Does this show feet or feed? _____

_____
- - - - - - - - - - - - - - - - - -
3. Is this a he or a she? _____

_____
- - - - - - - - - - - - - - - - - -
4. Is this a seed or a seat? _____

© Macmillan/McGraw-Hill

 At Home: Have your child illustrate the words that were not used in the sentences: *beak, feed, he, seat.*

Name _____

| knew | kind | house | friends |
| by | far | curious | idea |

Read each sentence. Circle the word that completes it.

1. Dan plays with ___.

    friends   curious

2. "I ___ it!" said Jan.

    knew   far

3. They came ___.

    by   knew

4. Ben is ___.

    curious   house

5. What ___ is it?

    far   kind

6. He has an ___.

    idea   far

7. Jan can run ___.

    far   idea

8. We have fun at Dan's ___.

    house   kind

At Home: Have your child think of another sentence using one of the words in the box.

Name _____

**As you read <u>Meet Ben Franklin</u>, fill in the
Inference Chart.**

Text Clues	What You Know	Inferences

**How does the Inference Chart help you better
understand <u>Meet Ben Franklin</u>?**

At Home: Have your child use the chart to retell the story.

Name _____

You can use what you read and what you already know to help you better understand a story.

Read each sentence. Circle the picture that answers the question.

1. She wants to play outside. Why can't she?

2. The dog wants to eat. What can the dog eat?

3. The bird makes a nest. Where is the nest?

4. The duck wants to swim. Why can't it swim?

 At Home: Ask your child to explain the answer to each question.

Meet Ben Franklin • **Book 1.4/Unit 4** 157

Name _____

As I read, I will pay attention to the punctuation.

	Meet Mae Jemison.
3	She is an astronaut.
7	As a little girl, Mae knew a lot
15	about the stars.
18	Mae liked to look at the stars from her
27	house. 28

Comprehension Check

1. Who is Mae Jemison?

2. What did Mae like to look at?

	Words Read	–	Number of Errors	=	Words Correct Score
First Read		–		=	
Second Read		–		=	

 At Home: Help your child read the passage, paying attention to the goal at the top of the page.

Name _____

A verb is a word that shows action. Sometimes verbs have the endings **–ing** and **–ed**.

Example: play **+ ed** = play**ed**   play **+ ing** = play**ing**

Write the verb with its ending.

1. pull + ed =

_____

- - - - - - - - - - - - - - - - - - -

_____

2. pull + ing =

_____

- - - - - - - - - - - - - - - - - - -

_____

3. flash + ed =

_____

- - - - - - - - - - - - - - - - - - -

_____

4. flash + ing =

_____

- - - - - - - - - - - - - - - - - - -

_____

5. fill + ed =

_____

- - - - - - - - - - - - - - - - - - -

_____

6. fill + ing =

_____

- - - - - - - - - - - - - - - - - - -

_____

Draw a picture that shows the meaning of one of the words that you wrote.

At Home: Think about the words *talk* and *listen*. Say each word with the endings *–ed* and *–ing*.

Read the words. Listen for the **long e** sound in each word.

s**ee**d   f**ee**t   l**ea**f   s**ea**t

**Write a word from the box to answer each riddle.
Then draw a line from each word to its picture.**

1. I drop from a tree.

   _____

   - - - - - - - - - - - - - - -

   What am I? _____

2. You put me in the dirt.

   _____

   - - - - - - - - - - - - - - -

   What am I? _____

3. You sit on me.

   _____

   - - - - - - - - - - - - - - -

   What am I? _____

4. I help you jump.

   _____

   - - - - - - - - - - - - - - -

   What am I? _____

© Macmillan/McGraw-Hill

At Home: Have your child think of two more words with the CVVC pattern.

Bold print points out important words.

A **cub** is a baby bear.

Read the story. Write the words in bold print that point out the important ideas in the story.

A cub lives in the **wild**, or outside. A cub goes to sleep when there is snow. It may sleep in a **cave**, or a hole in a hill.

Soon, it will be warm. The snow will **melt**, or go away. Then the cub will wake up. It will **hunt**, or look to eat.

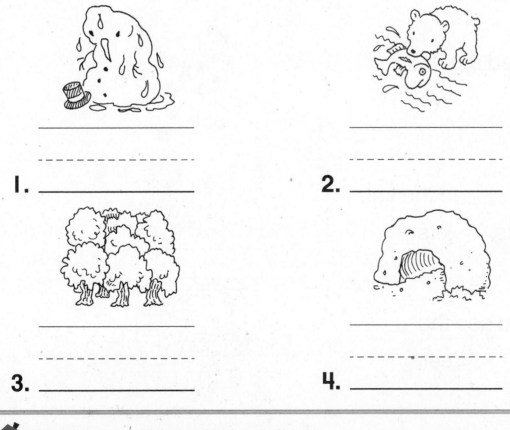

1. _____

2. _____

3. _____

4. _____

 At Home: Have your child browse through a magazine or newspaper and find words in bold print. Ask your child to explain why the words are in bold print.

Meet Ben Franklin • **Book 1.4/Unit 4** ★ 161

Name _____

The letters **ee**, **ea**, and **e** can stand for the long **e** sound as in **feet**, **leaf**, and **be**.

The letter **e** can stand for the short **e** sound as in **ten**.

Circle the word that completes each sentence.

1. My pet gets ____.

    fed   beak

2. The ____ is wet.

    seal   met

3. ____ need a net.

    She   We

4. My dad ____ to the vet.

    speaks   jets

5. Can you see the ____?

    set   eel

 At Home: Have your child sort the words from this page by their long *e* and short *e* vowel sounds.

Name _____

Read the word. The letter **y** stands for the long **e** sound at the end of **daisy**.

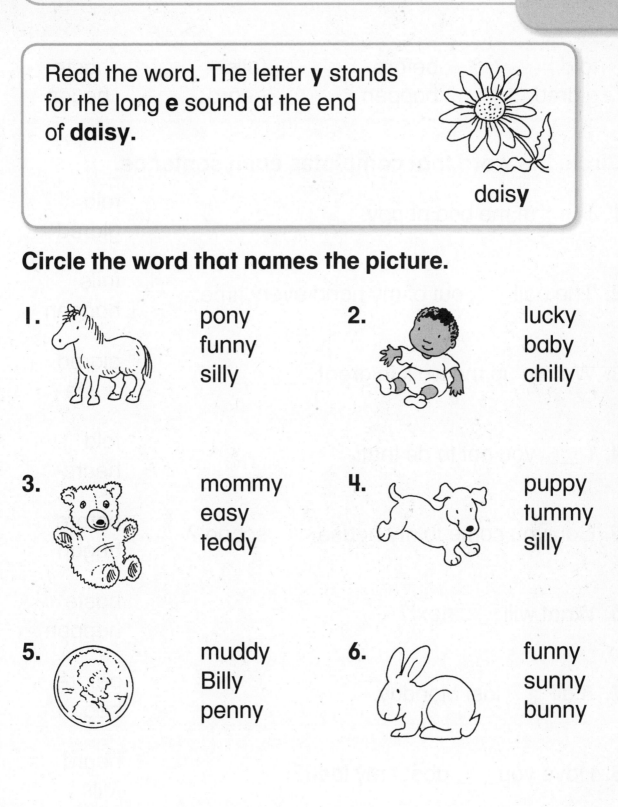

dais**y**

Circle the word that names the picture.

1.
pony
funny
silly

2.
lucky
baby
chilly

3.
mommy
easy
teddy

4.
puppy
tummy
silly

5.
muddy
Billy
penny

6.
funny
sunny
bunny

At Home: Have your child read all the words on the page.

Name _____

told	before	falls	haste
glared	happen	heard	began

Circle the word that completes each sentence.

1. I ____ at the bad puppy.

told
glared

2. The ball ____ out of my hand every time.

falls
happen

3. We ran up the walk in great ____.

glared
haste

4. I ____ you not to do that!

told
heard

5. Can you come to my house ____ school?

before
began

6. What will ____ next?

haste
happen

7. It all ____ last Monday.

before
began

8. Have you ____ about my idea?

heard
falls

© Macmillan/McGraw-Hill

At Home: Help your child use one of the words in the box in a new sentence.

Name _____

As you read <u>Little Rabbit</u>, fill in the Beginning, Middle, and End Chart.

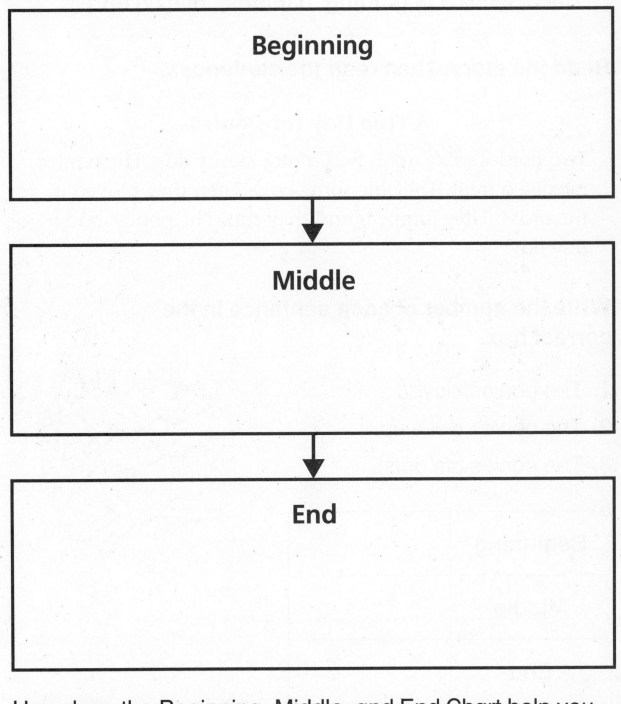

Beginning

↓

Middle

↓

End

How does the Beginning, Middle, and End Chart help you better understand <u>Little Rabbit</u>?

 At Home: Have your child use the chart to retell the story.

Little Rabbit • **Book 1.4/Unit 4** **165**

© Macmillan/McGraw-Hill

> The **plot** is what happens in a story.
> The plot has a **beginning**, a **middle**, and an **end**.

Read the story. Then read the sentences.

A Fine Day for Ponies

Two ponies woke up. It was a nice sunny day. The ponies needed a treat. They ate some oats. Then they played in the grass. They jumped, and they ran. The ponies had a fine day.

Write the number of each sentence in the correct box.

1. The ponies played.

2. The ponies woke up.

3. The ponies ate oats.

Beginning	
Middle	
End	

 At Home: Ask your child to retell the story using his or her own words. Remind your child to think about what happened in the beginning, middle, and end.

As I read, I will pay attention to patterns in the passage.

8	Every day, Ant worked in haste. She saved a lot of corn.
12	Soon snow began to fall. Grasshopper
18	looked for something to eat.
23	But he did not see a thing. 30

Comprehension Check

1. What did Ant do?

2. What did Grasshopper look for when it snowed?

	Words Read	−	Number of Errors	=	Words Correct Score
First Read		−		=	
Second Read		−		=	

At Home: Help your child read the passage, paying attention to the goal at the top of the page.

© Macmillan/McGraw-Hill

> **Context clues** are words in a sentence that help you figure out the meaning of a new word.

Use the <u>underlined</u> context clues to figure out the word from the box that completes the sentence. Write the word on the line.

forest	before	falling	heard

1. The <u>tall</u> <u>trees</u> <u>fill</u> the _____.

2. <u>We</u> _____ the <u>birds</u> <u>chirp</u> a <u>song</u>.

3. <u>Rain</u> <u>started</u> _____ <u>from</u> the <u>sky</u>.

4. I'm <u>glad</u> <u>we</u> <u>picked</u> the <u>berries</u> _____ the <u>rain</u> <u>started</u>.

© Macmillan/McGraw-Hill

At Home: Look at words on the page of a magazine. Help your child to use context clues to figure out the meaning of three unknown words.

When a word ends in **y**, change the **y** to **i** and add **-es** to tell more than one person or thing.

When a word ends in **y**, change the **y** to **i** and add **-es** to tell what one person or thing does.

pon**y**   pon**ies**

Circle the word that completes each sentence.

1.
I got a new ___.
puppy   puppies

2.
The ___ are in the nest.
bunny   bunnies

3.
The horse ___ to its pal.
whinny   whinnies

4.
Jenny gave Mom a ___.
daisy   daisies

5.
I have some shiny ___.
penny   pennies

© Macmillan/McGraw-Hill

 At Home: Say one of the words that ends in *y*. Have your child explain how to add *-es* to the word.

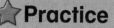
> **Repetition** is when some words or sentences in a story are used again and again.

Read the story. Draw a line around the word groups that show repetition.

Who Can Hop?

A frog can hop.
Hop! Hop! Hop!

A bunny can hop.
Hop! Hop! Hop!

A bug can hop.
Hop! Hop! Hop!

Can you hop?
Draw yourself hopping.

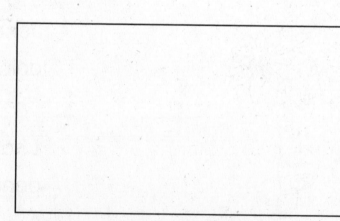

 At Home: Read the story aloud with your child. Have your child read the repeated word groups that are circled.

Name _____

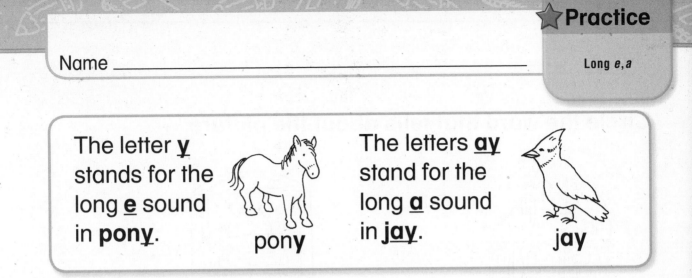

The letter **y** stands for the long **e** sound in **pony**.

pony

The letters **ay** stand for the long **a** sound in **jay**.

jay

Read the words in the puzzle.
Color shapes with words that end with the long e sound green.
Color the long a sound brown.

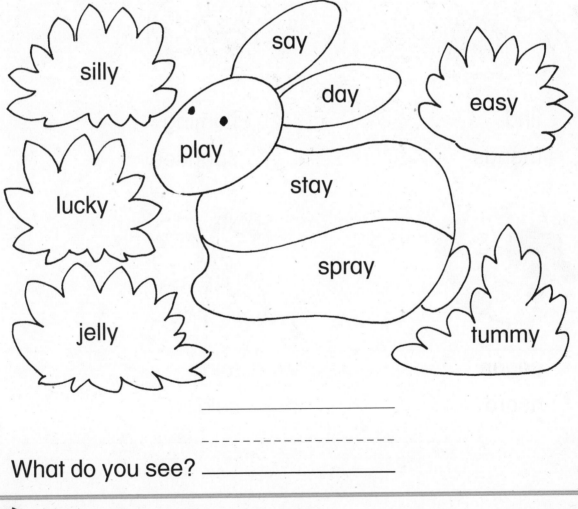

silly

say

day

easy

play

stay

lucky

spray

jelly

tummy

_____

- - - - - - - - - - - - - - - - - -

What do you see? _____

 At Home: On the puzzle, have your child circle the letter that
stands for the long *e* sound. Have your child underline the
letters that stand for the long *a* sound.

Little Rabbit • **Book 1.4/Unit 4** ★ **171**

© Macmillan/McGraw-Hill

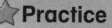
Circle the word that tells about the picture.

1.

sound

house

2.

warm

terrific

3.

find

friends

4.

floating

sparkled

5.

began

heard

6.

told

cold

Name _____

Write a word from the box that is the opposite of each word in the first column.

1. warm

_____

- - - - - - - - - - - - - - - - - -

_____

2. old

_____

- - - - - - - - - - - - - - - - - -

_____

3. near

_____

- - - - - - - - - - - - - - - - - -

_____

4. before

_____

- - - - - - - - - - - - - - - - - -

_____

5. closed

_____

- - - - - - - - - - - - - - - - - -

_____

far

cold

after

opened

new

Name _____

Read the words.
Listen for the long <u>o</u> sound.

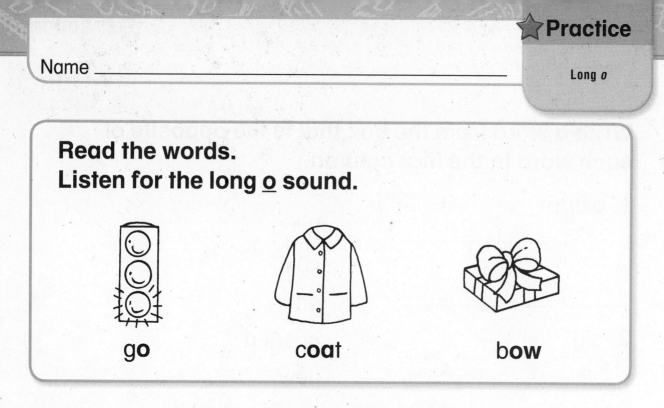

go   coat   bow

Circle the word that matches the picture.

1.   goat   got   2.   snow   snap

3.   cot   crow   4.   soap   sop

5.   row   road   6.   toad   to

At Home: Write the long *o* words on a sheet of paper. Have your child circle the letters that make the long *o* sound.

© Macmillan/McGraw-Hill

Name _____

Circle the word that completes each sentence.
Write the word on the line.

1. My _____ likes to have fun.

   mother
   most

2. Mom has to be _____, too.

   firm
   find

3. She _____ loves me.

   ask
   always

4. My _____ made a plane.

   fast
   father

5. It is _____ to go fast.

   supposed
   sun

6. He will _____ to fix it.

   trick
   try

7. My mom and dad _____ me.

   loan
   love

 At Home: Encourage your child to tell things that he or she is supposed to do.

Olivia • Book 1.5/Unit 5   175

Name _____

As you read <u>Olivia</u>, fill in the Fantasy and Reality Chart.

Reality	Fantasy
What Happens	**Why It Could Not Happen In Real Life**

How does the Fantasy and Reality Chart help you better understand <u>Olivia</u>?

176 Olivia • **Book I.5/Unit 5**

 At Home: Have your child use the chart to retell the story.

© Macmillan/McGraw-Hill

Reality is something that could really happen.

Fantasy is something make believe and could not really happen.

reality   fantasy

Color the pictures that show <u>reality</u>.

1.

2.

3.

4.

5.

6.

 At Home: Read a book with your child. Talk about things
that are real and things that are make believe.

Olivia • **Book 1.5/Unit 5**   177

As I read, I will pay attention to pauses for punctuation.

	"I love to play hopscotch," said Maria.
7	"I'll throw the first stone," said Joan.
14	The stone landed on the first square.
21	Joan hopped over that square. Then she
28	hopped to the end. Then Joan shut her eyes.
37	And when she opened them, she saw some
45	people. They had on funny outfits. Joan did,
53	too! They looked just like the people in the
62	new painting! 64

Comprehension Check

1. What game do Sally and her friends play?

2. How can you tell that Sally is in a new place?

	Words Read	−	Number of Errors	=	Words Correct Score
First Read		−		=	
Second Read		−		=	

At Home: Help your student read the passage, paying attention to the goal at the top of the page.

© Macmillan/McGraw-Hill

Name _____

Read the dictionary entries below. Circle the correct word in the ( ) to complete the sentences.

prefer to like better: I **prefer** to play soccer over baseball.

protects to keep away from harm: The mother hen **protects** her nest of eggs.

relax to rest: The girls will **relax** under the shady tree.

1. The mother fox (relax, protects) her little ones.

2. The fox family likes to (relax, prefer) in the sun.

3. The little foxes (protects, prefer) to jump and play.

At Home: As you read together, find a word your child doesn't know. Work together to find the meaning of the word in the dictionary.

Olivia • **Book 1.5/Unit 5**

Name _____

Adding the letter **y** to the end of some words makes a new word.

Notice that the **y** stands for the **long e** sound.

snow + **y** = snow**y**

Write the new word on the line. Draw a line to the picture that matches each new word.

1. soap + y = _____

2. toast + y = _____

3. stick + y = _____

4. fuss + y = _____

Use one of the new words in a sentence.

_____

_____

© Macmillan/McGraw-Hill

Name _____

Read the three captions below. Write the correct caption under each picture.

Hens and ducks lay eggs.

Cows, pigs, and goats live on farms.

A sheep is a big animal.

1. _____

2. _____

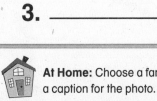

3. _____

At Home: Choose a family photograph. Help your child write a caption for the photo.

Name _____

Circle the word that matches the picture.

1. Is this a boat or a block?

2. Is this a bow or a boy?

3. Is this a rod or a road?

4. Is this a pile or a pillow?

5. Is this a cot or a coat?

6. Is this a window or a willow?

7. Is this stop or go?

8. Is this a note or a nose?

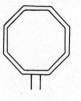

© Macmillan/McGraw-Hill

 At Home: Help your child tell a story about a toad in a hole. What long *o* and short *o* words can be added to the story?

Name _____

What letters stand for the **long i** sound in these words?

child
the letter **i**

fly
the letter **y**

high
the letters **igh**

Read each word.
Underline the letters that stand for the <u>long i</u> sound.
Write the letters on the line.

1. _____
   cry

2. _____
   tight

3. _____
   bright

4. _____
   wind

5. **?** _____
   why

6. _____
   wild

 At Home: Have your child write a word with the same long *i* vowel pattern as in *fly*, in *high*, and in *child*.

Circle the word that completes each sentence.

1. The _____ was hit high.
   ball   head

2. The boy will _____ get the ball.
   never   should

3. _____ we can have a picnic.
   Ball   Perhaps

4. Let's eat in the green _____ .
   head   meadow

5. The boys and girls will _____ at the game today.
   never   shout

6. Matt is waving his hand over his _____ .
   head   never

7. The school bus _____ be here on time.
   meadow   should

8. There was a lot of _____ in the big tent.
   head   laughter

 At Home: Have your child make up another sentence using one of the vocabulary words.

As you read <u>The Kite</u>, fill in the Problem and Solution Chart.

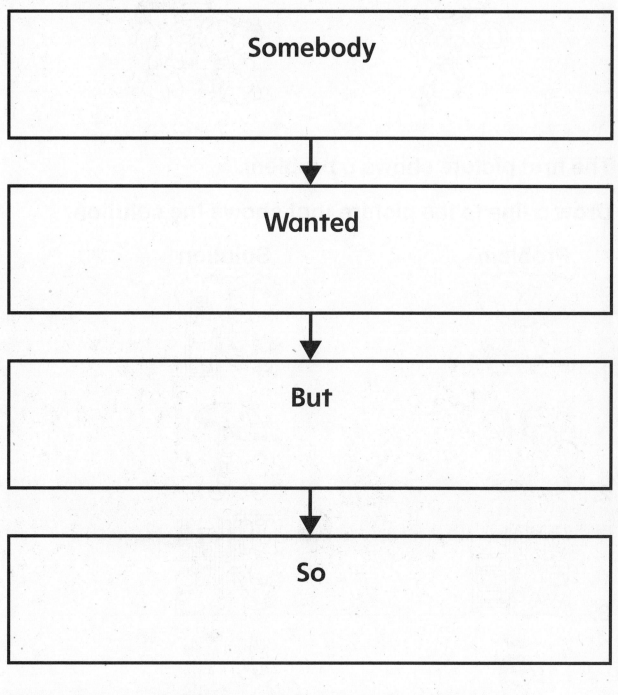

Somebody

Wanted

But

So

How does the Problem and Solution Chart help you better understand <u>The Kite</u>?

 At Home: Have your child use the chart to retell the story.

The Kite • **Book 1.5/Unit 5**   185

Name _____

Problem	Solution

The first picture shows a problem.

Draw a line to the picture that shows the solution.

Problem	Solution

1.

2.

3.

4.

 At Home: Have your child talk about the problem and
solution in one of the picture sequences.

As I read, I will pay attention to dialogue.

	On Tuesday, Teddy heard Pam shout.
6	"My doll fell into the water," Pam shouted.
14	The doll's head was all wet.
20	Teddy pulled her out.
24	Teddy saved the day!
28	On Wednesday, Teddy heard Matt shout.
34	Matt shouted, "The glue spilled all over the
42	table." Mouse was going into the glue. Teddy
50	pushed Mouse away. Teddy saved the day! 57

Comprehension Check

1. How did Teddy get the doll out of the water?

2. What would have happened to Mouse if Teddy had not saved him?

	Words Read	−	Number of Errors	=	Words Correct Score
First Read		−		=	
Second Read		−		=	

At Home: Help your student read the passage, paying attention to the goal at the top of the page.

Name _____

A verb is a word that shows action. When a verb has the ending **–ed**, the action happened in the past. The **–ing** ending means the action is happening now. You can pick out the word parts of a verb to figure out its meaning.

Underline the base word in each verb.
Write <u>now</u> if the action is happening now.
Write <u>past</u> if the action happened in the past.

For example: <u>open</u>ed - past   <u>open</u>ing - now

1. resting _____

2. mowed _____

3. climbing _____

4. filled _____

5. mixing _____

At Home: Talk with your child about some things he or she did today. Pay attention to the verbs that end in *–ed*.

© Macmillan/McGraw-Hill

When you add **-er** or **-est** to words that end in **e**, drop the **e** before adding **-er** or **-est**.

Cut**e** + **er** = cut**er**   My dog is **cuter** than my cat.

Cut**e** + **est** = cut**est**   My pup is the **cutest** of all.

Circle the word that completes each sentence.
Write the word on the line.

1. My kite is _____ than Sam's kite.   whiteer   whiter

2. This grape is the _____ in the bunch.   ripest   ripeest

3. This lake is _____ right here.   widest   wideest

4. This wild dog is _____ than my pup.   braver   braveer

5. Sam is the _____ cat of all.
   niceest   nicest

© Macmillan/McGraw-Hill

Name _____

Look at the diagram of a fish. Use the words from the box to complete the diagram. Write the words on the correct lines.

fin	scales	head

_____

- - - - - - - - - - - - - - - -

I. _____

_____

- - - - - - - - - - - - - - - -

2. _____

_____

- - - - - - - - - - - - - - - -

3. _____

© Macmillan/McGraw-Hill

At Home: Have your child tell you other ways that Sam and Max are the same and different.

Name _____

Say the words.

Listen to the **long *i*** sound.

     m**i**ld   m**y**   fl**igh**t

Listen to the **short *i*** sound.

     s**i**t

Complete each word by writing the letters <u>i</u>, <u>igh</u>, or <u>y</u>.

1. ch _____ ld

2. f _____ n

3. fl _____

4. h _____

5. m _____ tt

6. w _____ nd

At Home: Have your child write one more word with the long vowel sound spelled *i*, *igh*, or *y* and the short vowel sound spelled *i*.

© Macmillan/McGraw-Hill

Together the letters **a** and **r** stand for the sound you hear in **car**.

c**ar**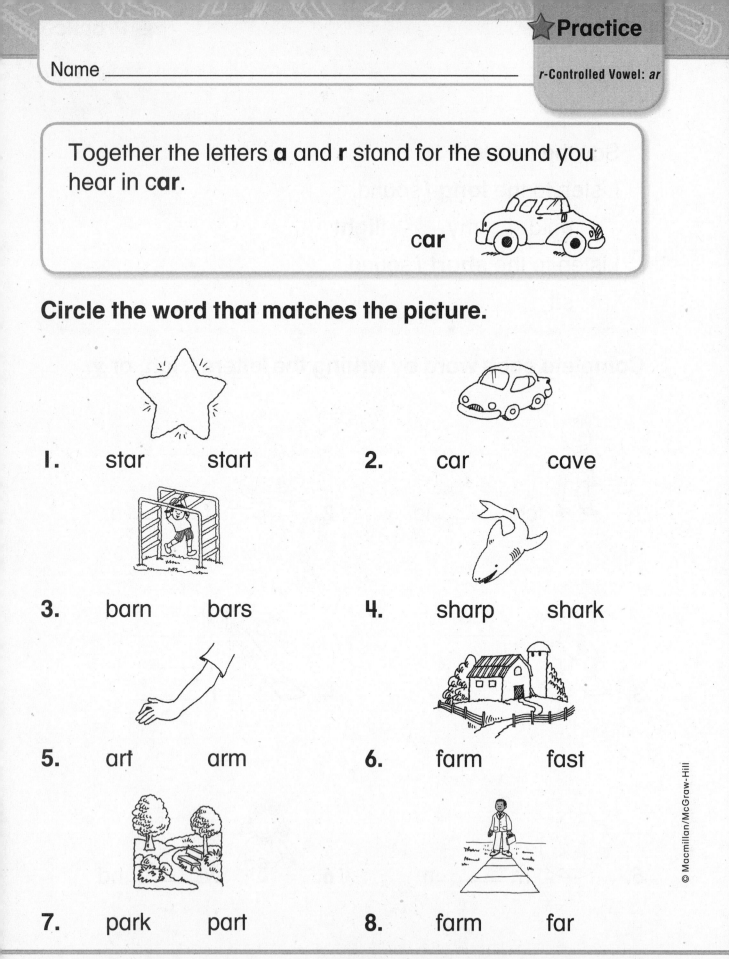

Circle the word that matches the picture.

1. star   start

2. car   cave

3. barn   bars

4. sharp   shark

5. art   arm

6. farm   fast

7. park   part

8. farm   far

© Macmillan/McGraw-Hill

 At Home: Have your child name a rhyming word for each circled word.

Read the sentences and look at the picture below. Match each sentence to the word that completes it.

1. Some _____ went on a hunt.   round

2. They made a _____.   better

3. It was big and _____.   discovery

4. It was a _____ with a note on it.   children

5. The note said, "This will make sick pets _____."   machine

6. Carlos asked his friends a _____.   or

7. Should we switch it on _____ off?   question

At Home: Have your child draw a picture of a machine that helps animals.

Kids' Inventions
Book 1.5/Unit 5

193

© Macmillan/McGraw-Hill

As you read <u>Kids' Inventions</u>, fill in the Cause and Effect Chart.

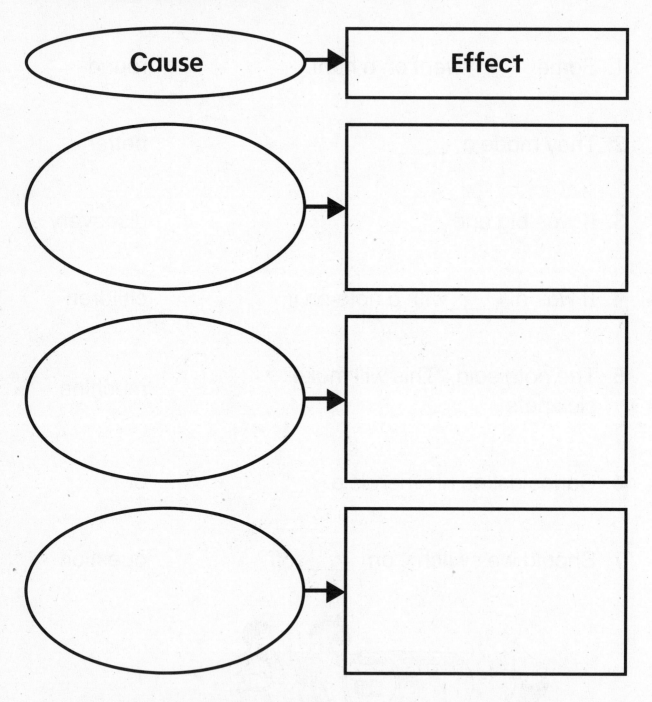

Cause

Effect

How does the Cause and Effect Chart help you better understand <u>Kids' Inventions</u>?

 At Home: Have your child use the chart to retell the story.

© Macmillan/McGraw-Hill

Name _____

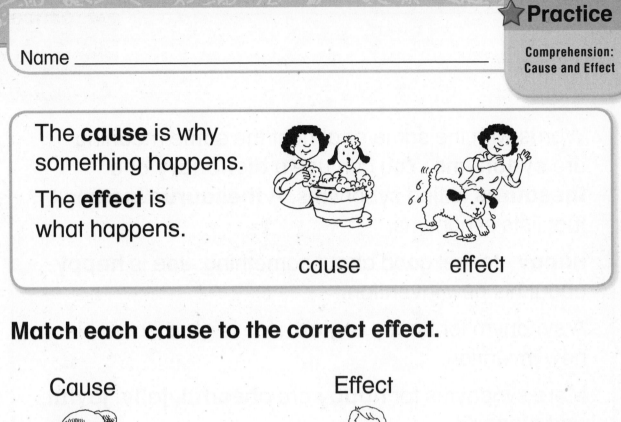

The **cause** is why something happens.

The **effect** is what happens.

cause   effect

Match each cause to the correct effect.

Cause	Effect

1.   

2.

3.

4.

5.

 At Home: Have your child tell a different effect for each of the causes.

Words with the same or almost the same meaning are **synonyms**. You can use a **dictionary** or a **thesaurus** to find synonyms. A **thesaurus** is a book that lists synonyms.

happy to feel good about something: Joe is **happy** about his new invention.

A synonym for happy is **glad:** Joe is **glad** about his new invention.

More synonyms for **happy** are **cheerful, jolly, joyful,** and **pleased.**

Read each sentence circle the word that means the same as the underlined word.

1. Kim is a very <u>smart</u> girl.

   clever   funny

2. She can sing a <u>song</u> very well.

   school   tune

3. She won a prize from the <u>game</u>.

   contest   ball

 At Home: Have your child think of two synonyms for *funny.* Then say a silly sentence using these words.

© Macmillan/McGraw-Hill

As I read, I will pay attention to the question.

	Young children long ago wanted to ride
7	bicycles, too. They learned to ride on tricycles.
15	A tricycle has three wheels. Today young
22	children ride tricycles, too. This is how small
30	children learn to ride. Today people ride all
38	kinds of bicycles. Now you know all about
46	bicycles. What will bicycles look like when
53	you grow up? That's a good question! One
61	day you could make a bicycle discovery! 68

Comprehension Check

1. What is different about a tricycle?

2. What might a bicycle that you invented look like?

	Words Read	−	Number of Errors	=	Words Correct Score
First Read		−		=	
Second Read		−		=	

At Home: Help your child read the passage, paying attention to the goal at the top of the page.

Kids' Inventions
Book 1.5/Unit 5

A **card catalog** helps you find books in a library.

Electronic Card Catalog

A. Call Number FIC L 2
B. Author Lions, Misty
C. Title The Sad Bug

D. Summary A book about a bug and his helpful friends

A. These numbers show where you can find the book in the library.

B. author's name

C. title of book

D. what the book is about

Look at the card catalog page.
Read each sentence. Write or circle the correct answer.

1. Who is the author?

_____

- -

_____

2. What is the title?

_____

- -

_____

3. This part tells where the book is.   A B C D

4. This part tells what the book is about.   A B C D

At Home: Have your child make a card catalog page for his or her favorite book.

Name _____

An **abbreviation** is a short form of writing a longer word.
Look at these abbreviations.

Mister → Mr.   Saturday → Sat.   Doctor → Dr.

Match the word to the correct abbreviation.

1. Mister   Dr.

2. Saturday   Mr.

3. Doctor   Sat.

Write an abbreviation for the underlined word.

4. Did you visit <u>Doctor</u> Hall?   _____

5. <u>Mister</u> Jon is my dad.   _____

6. Can I go to Nan's home on <u>Saturday</u>?   _____

 At Home: Help your child tell the titles for different family
and friends.

Match the words to the correct picture.

1. a car in the rain

2. a carp in a pail

3. a scarf in the mail

4. a lake with a shark

5. a park with shade

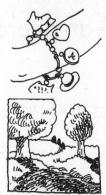

6. a charm bracelet on an arm

7. a star on a hat

8. a man at a park

 At Home: Circle all of the *ar* words.

Look at the picture. The letters **or** stand for the middle sound in **storm** and **horse**.

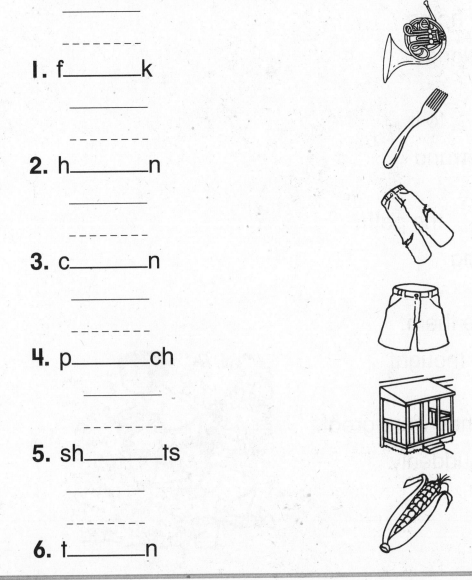

Write the letters <u>or</u> to complete each word.

Read the word and draw a line to its picture.

1. f_____k

2. h_____n

3. c_____n

4. p_____ch

5. sh_____ts

6. t_____n

 At Home: Have your child write one more word that has the same middle sound as *horse*.

Whistle for Willie • **Book 1.5/Unit 5**

 201

Circle the word that completes each sentence.

1. We get up _____.

   nothing   early

2. We can do an _____ for Mom.

   along   errand

3. She can stay home _____.

   instead   along

4. There is _____ to it.

   nothing   errand

5. We walk _____ the path.

   early   along

6. _____ we see them.

   suddenly   thought

7. Mom _____ they were great.

   thought   suddenly

At Home: Have your child use one of the circled words in a sentence.

© Macmillan/McGraw-Hill

Name _____

As you read <u>Whistle for Willie</u>, fill in the Inference Chart.

Text Clues	What You Know	Inferences

How does the Inference Chart help you better understand <u>Whistle for Willie</u>?

At Home: Have your child use the chart to retell the story.

Name _____

> You can use what you read and what you already know to help you better understand a story.

Read the sentences. Circle the sentence that tells what the people in the picture are doing.

1. We are going to school.

We are going to play.

2. I am cooking dinner.

I am going to work.

3. We are going to the beach.

We are going skating.

4. We are going to bed.

We are going for a walk.

5. We are going to school.

We are going camping.

 At Home: Have your child draw a picture that includes items to be packed for a picnic at a park.

Name _____

As I read, I will pay attention to pauses for punctuation.

	Katie looked at the dolphins on Matt's shirt.
8	"Would you like to swim like a dolphin?"
16	Katie asked.
18	"I would," said Matt. "But I don't think I can,"
28	Matt thought. "Here's something for you,"
34	said Katie.
36	"Thanks," said Matt.
39	Early the next day, Matt and Dad walked
47	along the water. Then they swam just like
55	dolphins! 56

Comprehension Check

1. What does Matt think of swimming?

2. How do you know that Matt learns to swim?

	Words Read	–	Number of Errors	=	Words Correct Score
First Read		–		=	
Second Read		–		=	

At Home: Help your child read the passage, paying attention to the goal at the top of the page.

Whistle for Willie • **Book 1.5/Unit 5**

205

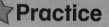
A **base word** is the word that is left when you remove the **–ed** or **–ing** ending. You can use the base word to figure out the meaning of a word.

Sasha **pretended** to be a famous dancer.

The base word is **pretend.**

pretend means to make believe

Circle the base word in each row.

Example: glided (glide) gliding

1. whirled   whirling   whirl
2. push   pushing   pushed
3. answering   answer   answered
4. wishing   wished   wish
5. looked   look   looking

Match each base word to its meaning.

6. whirl   **a.** to press or move

7. push   **b.** to see

8. answer   **c.** to hope for

9. wish   **d.** to spin quickly

10. look   **e.** to respond

 At Home: Say three sentences using the words *look, looked,* and *looking.*

Name _____

If a verb ends in a consonant + **y**, change the **y** to **i** before you add **ed**.

cr**y** + ed = cr**i**ed

Read the word under each sentence. Change the word by adding ed. Then complete each sentence.

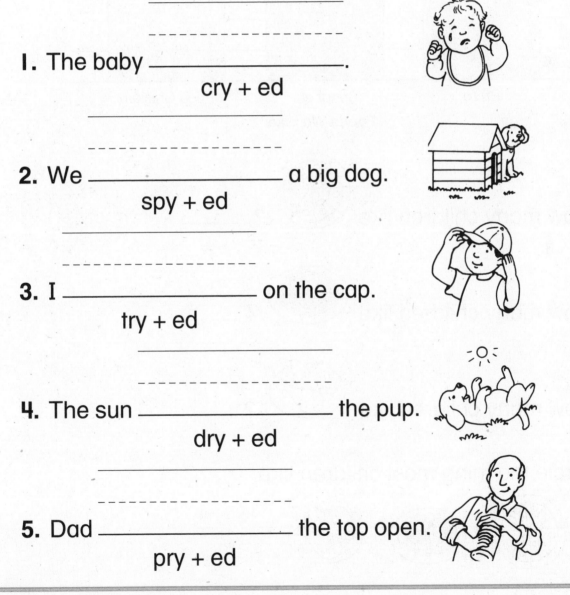

_____

- - - - - - - - - - - - - - - - - -

1. The baby _____.

          cry + ed

_____

- - - - - - - - - - - - - - - - - -

2. We _____ a big dog.

          spy + ed

_____

- - - - - - - - - - - - - - - - - -

3. I _____ on the cap.

          try + ed

_____

- - - - - - - - - - - - - - - - - -

4. The sun _____ the pup.

          dry + ed

_____

- - - - - - - - - - - - - - - - - -

5. Dad _____ the top open.

          pry + ed

© Macmillan/McGraw-Hill

At Home: Have your child use one of the words in the box in a sentence.

Whistle for Willie • Book 1.5/Unit 5

A **graph** can show how many of something.

Read the bar graph. Then answer the questions.

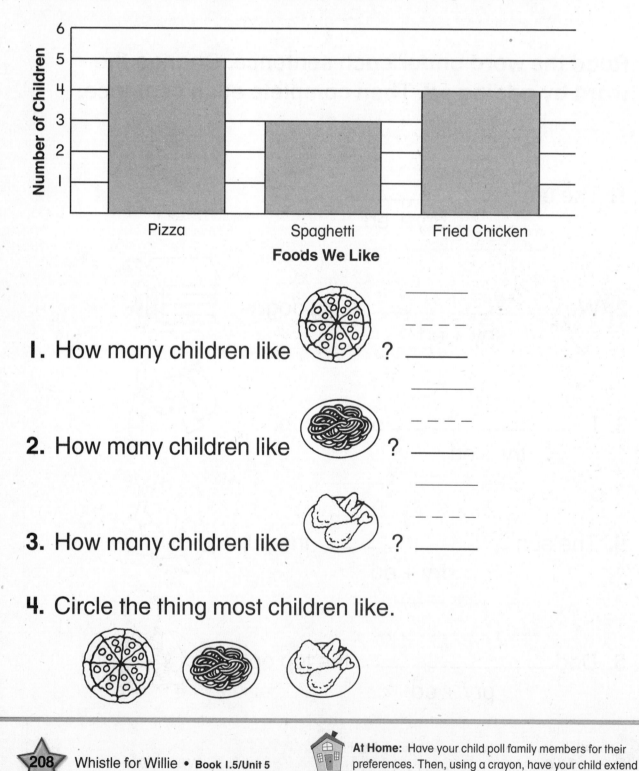

Foods We Like

1. How many children like 🍕 ? _____

2. How many children like 🍝 ? _____

3. How many children like 🍗 ? _____

4. Circle the thing most children like.

At Home: Have your child poll family members for their preferences. Then, using a crayon, have your child extend the bars on the graph.

© Macmillan/McGraw-Hill

The letters **or** stand for the middle sound in **born**.

The letters **ar** stand for the middle sound in **barn**.

Circle the word that completes each sentence.

1. I am at the ___.

farm   form

2. I help in the ___.

born   barn

3. I pick the ___.

card   corn

4. I ___ the peas and beans.

sort   start

At Home: Have your child find pictures in magazines of words with the *or* and *ar* vowel sounds. Then ask your child to sort the pictures and paste the pictures onto an *ar* or *or* sheet.

The letters **er**, **ir**, and **ur** can stand for the same sound.

fern　　　　　　　**girl**　　　　　　　**curl**

Draw a line from the word to the picture it names.

1. bird

2. her

3. shirt

4. curl

5. thirty

6. herd

 At Home: Have your child read the words and trace over the *er, ir,* or *ur*.

© Macmillan/McGraw-Hill

Name _____

Use words from the box to complete each sentence.

animals	beautiful	crowded	from
part	places	tiny	ground

1. I have visited many _____.

2. Look at the _____ rose on the

   _____.

3. I can walk to school _____ my home.

4. There are too many pigs in the _____
   pen.

5. Dogs and cats are _____.

6. An ant ate a _____ _____ of my lunch.

 At Home: Give clues for each word and have
your child guess the word.

A Fruit Is a Suitcase for Seeds **211**
Book 1.5/Unit 5

© Macmillan/McGraw-Hill

Name _____

As you read <u>A Fruit is a Suitcase for Seeds</u>, fill in the Classify and Categorize Chart

Classify and Categorize	
One Seed	**Many Seeds**

How does the Classify and Categorize Chart help you better understand <u>A Fruit is a Suitcase for Seeds</u>?

© Macmillan/McGraw-Hill

 At Home: Have your child use the chart to retell the story.

Things that are alike in some way go together.

A **skirt** and a **shirt** go together because they are both things people put on.

Look at the picture in the left column. Circle the picture in the right column that goes with it.

 At Home: Have your child explain why the circled pictures belong together.

A Fruit Is a Suitcase for Seeds
Book I.5/Unit 5

As I read, I will pay attention to patterns.

7	Apples grow on apple trees. Some apples are red.
9	Some are yellow.
12	Some are green.
15	For part of the winter, the ground is very
24	cold.
25	Apple trees have no leaves.
30	When spring comes, tiny buds grow. They
37	burst open. Then the tree has little flowers
45	and leaves.
47	Soon the apple tree becomes crowded with
54	beautiful flowers. 56

Comprehension Check

1. What colors are apples?

2. What happens to an apple tree in the spring?

	Words Read	–	Number of Errors	=	Words Correct Score
First Read		–		=	
Second Read		–		=	

 At Home: Help your child read the passage, paying attention to the goal at the top of the page.

Context clues are words that help you figure out the meaning of a new word. Context clues may be found in the same sentence or in nearby sentences.

Write the letter of the definition that shows the meaning of the underlined word or words.

a. back

b. very full

c. go to see or stay

1. All the toys <u>won't fit</u> in the suitcase. There is no room for the truck.

2. Jon likes to <u>visit</u> many places. He likes to go to his grandmother's house.

3. Oh no! The suitcase was left <u>behind</u>. It is not in the car.

 At Home: Talk about items you would pack into a suitcase if you were to travel on a vacation.

A Fruit Is a Suitcase for Seeds
Book 1.5/Unit 5
215

A **prefix** is a word part you can add to the beginning of a base word to change the meaning of the word.

The prefix **re-** means **again:**
re + tie = **re**tie.   to tie again

The prefix **un-** means **not** or **the opposite:**
un + likely = **un**likely.   not likely

Circle the prefix. Then write the meaning of each word.

1. u n s a f e _____

2. r e f i l l _____

3. r e t e l l _____

4. u n h a p p y _____

5. r e p a c k _____

© Macmillan/McGraw-Hill

At Home: Have your child fold, unfold, and refold a sheet of paper while saying, "I'm folding the paper," "I'm unfolding the paper," and "I'm refolding the paper."

Name _____

In some poems, the second line of a verse
rhymes with the fourth line.

**Circle the rhyming words in each poem. Then
write them on the lines.**

Look out for
The bees
In the buds
On the trees.

_____

- - - - - - - - - - - - - - - -

_____

Plants like
The rain,
But to me
It's a pain.

_____

- - - - - - - - - - - - - - - -

_____

What do you
Like to bake—
A pie or
A cake?

_____

- - - - - - - - - - - - - - - -

_____

I saw
A big frog.
It jumped over
A log.

_____

- - - - - - - - - - - - - - - -

_____

At Home: Help your child think of more pairs of
rhyming words.

When the letter **r** comes after a vowel, it changes the vowel sound.

had/h**ar**d   shot/sh**or**t   gem/g**er**m   fist/f**ir**st   cub/c**ur**b

Read the words in the row. Write the words in each group that have the same vowel sound.

1. curb   star   third   _____

_____

2. horn   fort   nerve   _____

_____

3. farm   burn   fern   _____

_____

4. car   hard   herd   _____

_____

5. verse   corn   squirm   _____

_____

6. sharp   sir   her   _____

At Home: Have your child think of another word to add to each group.

© Macmillan/McGraw-Hill

Underline the word that tells about the picture.

1.

animals

children

2.

ball

part

3.

father

mother

4.

meadow

mother

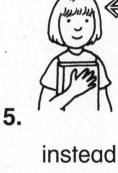

5.

instead

head

6.

machine

errand

© Macmillan/McGraw-Hill

Practice

Name ______________________________

Review: Words to Know

Write the word that completes each sentence.

1. A ball is ______________. along / round

2. Parks and meadows are ______________ places / always

3. Cats and birds are ______________ along / animals

4. I never like to get up ______________. early / beautiful

5. I ______________ of a good idea. try / thought

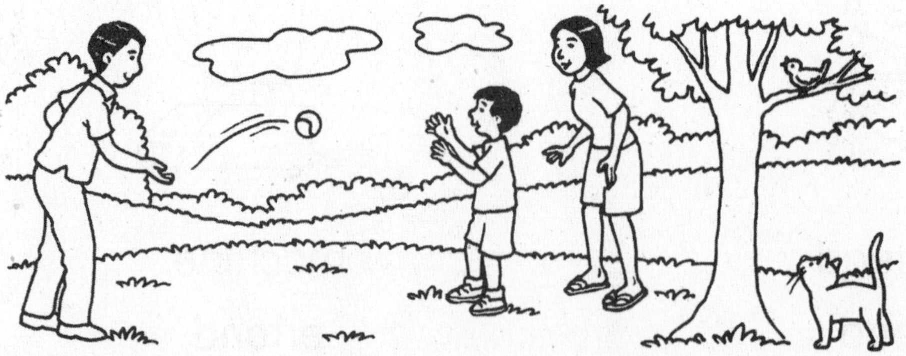

Look at the pictures.
The letters **ou** and **ow** stand for the vowel sounds in
h**ou**se and c**ow**.

house 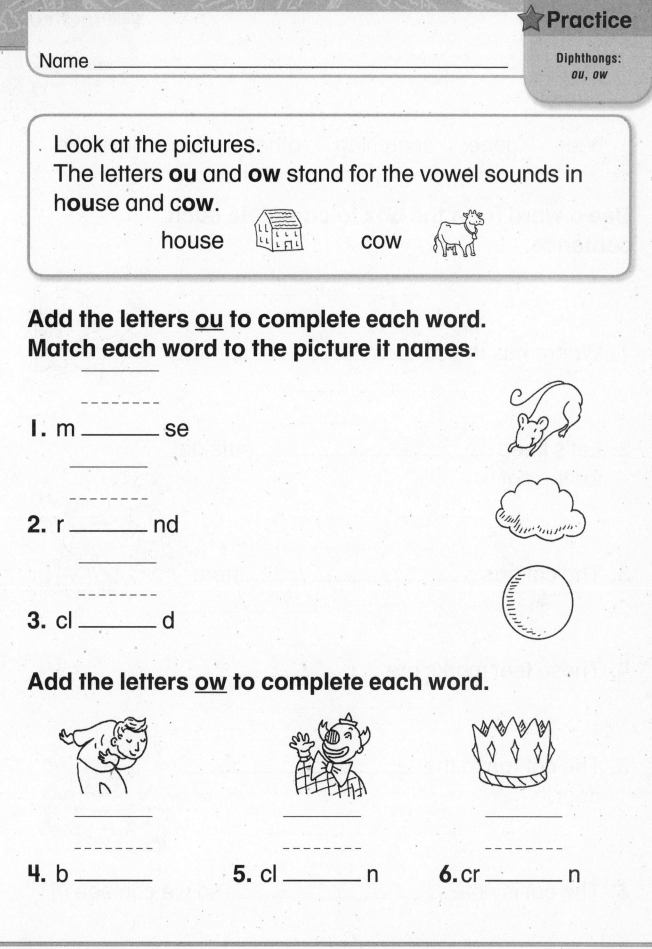 cow

Add the letters <u>ou</u> to complete each word.
Match each word to the picture it names.

1. m _____ se

2. r _____ nd

3. cl _____ d

Add the letters <u>ow</u> to complete each word.

4. b _____

5. cl _____ n

6. cr _____ n

Name _____

| been | gone | searching | other | clue | invisible |

Use a word from the box to complete each sentence.

_____

1. Where has the cat _____?

_____

2. Let's keep _____ outside for the cat.

_____

3. The cat has _____ here.

_____

4. These feet marks are _____.

_____

5. The cat ran to the _____ door.

_____

6. The cat is not _____ so we can see it!

At Home: Have your child make up a sentence for each word in the box.

Name _____

As you read <u>Dot and Jabber and the Big Bug Mystery</u>, fill in the Illustrations Chart.

Use Illustrations	
Illustration	**What It Shows**

How does the Illustrations Chart help you better understand <u>Dot and Jabber and the Big Bug Mystery</u>?

 At Home: Have your child use the chart to retell the story.

Dot and Jabber and the Big Bug Mystery • **Book 1.6/Unit 6** 223

© Macmillan/McGraw-Hill

You can use **illustrations,** or pictures, to help you better understand what you read.

Look at the picture of the ants.

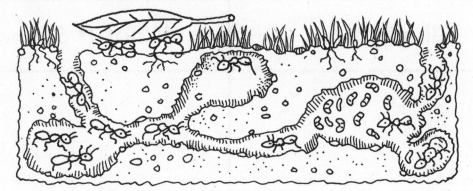

Circle the sentences that tell about the picture.

1. The ants are very big.

2. The ants walk past grass.

3. The dog runs after the ants.

4. The ants work together.

5. Ants dig paths under the ground.

6. Ants live in the sea.

Write another sentence that describes the picture.

_____

- -

_____

© Macmillan/McGraw-Hill

At Home: Ask your child to find a picture of an insect in a magazine or book. Ask him or her to tell details about the picture.

Name _____

As I read, I will pay attention to pauses for sentence punctuation.

	Bee flew away from her hive.
6	She flew from flower to flower.
12	Bee had been gone for a while. She wanted
21	to go back. But she could not find the hive.
31	"I need a clue," said Bee.
37	"I need to find other bees like me."
45	Bee went searching. She saw a red bug.
53	"It is not a bee like me," said Bee. 62

Comprehension Check

1. What is Bee looking for?

2. What color is the bug that Bee sees?

	Words Read	–	Number of Errors	=	Words Correct Score
First Read		–		=	
Second Read		–		=	

At Home: Help your child read the passage, paying attention to the goal at the top of the page.

Dot and Jabber and the Big Bug
Mystery • **Book 1.5/Unit 6**

A **dictionary** gives the meaning of a word, shows how to spell a word, and how to use it in a sentence.

clues hints that help solve a problem or a mystery: The dog's muddy pawprints were **clues** to finding him.

disappeared went away, out of sight: The clouds **disappeared** when the sun came out.

searching looking carefully: Dad is **searching** for his car keys.

Complete the sentence by circling the correct word in the ( ).

1. A slice of pie (mystery, disappeared) from the plate.

2. Mom follows a trail of crumbly (clues, mystery).

3. Tom searches for (clues, invisible) under the table.

4. Mom is (searching, disappeared) under the table, too.

© Macmillan/McGraw-Hill

At Home: Together, scan a book until you come to a few words your child doesn't know. Then look up their meanings in a dictionary.

Name _____

When a word has two consonants in the middle, divide the word between the consonants to read it.

puppet   pup • pet

Put the two word parts together. Write the word. Then match the word to the picture it names.

1. kit   ten   _____

2. bas   ket   _____

3. nap   kin   _____

4. pen   cil   _____

5. ham   mer   _____

6. mag   net   _____

© Macmillan/McGraw-Hill

 At Home: Have your child read each word aloud, dividing it into syllables.

Dot and Jabber and the Big Bug
Mystery • Book 1.5/Unit 6

 227

A **head** tells what information is in a section.

Read the article. Then answer the questions.

Spiders

A spider is a small animal. Spiders live all over the world.

The Body of a Spider

A spider has 2 body parts. An insect has 3 body parts. A spider has 8 legs. An insect has only 6. A spider is different from an insect.

The Home of a Spider

A spider spins a web and then stays in the web. The sticky web helps the spider catch food.

_____

- -

1. What is the article about? _____

2. List the 2 heads that tell about the different sections in the article.

_____

- -

_____

- -

_____

At Home: Have your child write two more sentences about spiders.

Read each word. Circle the pictures in each row. that have the same vowel sound.

1. found

2. dirt

  30

3. down

4. how

5. toad

 At Home: Have your child read each word aloud.

Read the words. The letters **oo** stand for the vowel sound in l**oo**k and b**oo**k.

L**oo**k at that big b**oo**k!

Circle the word that names each picture. Write the word.

1. 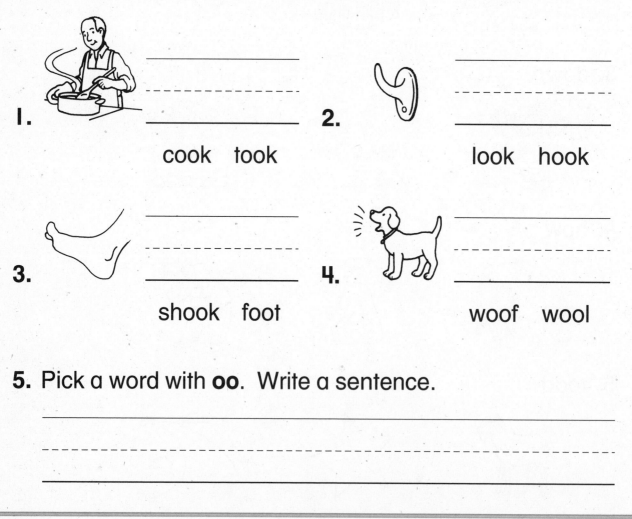 _____

   cook   took

2. _____

   look   hook

3. _____

   shook   foot

4. _____

   woof   wool

5. Pick a word with **oo**. Write a sentence.

_____

_____

 At Home: Have your child use each word in a sentence.

© Macmillan/McGraw-Hill

Name _____

Write the word that completes each question.

| bird | Earth | table | bear |
| fooling | guess | helmet | space |

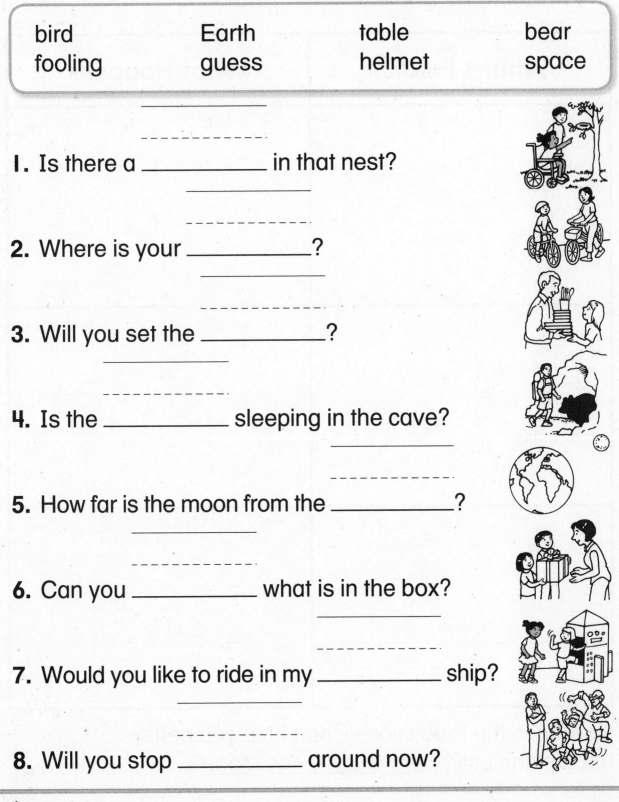

1. Is there a _____ in that nest?

2. Where is your _____?

3. Will you set the _____?

4. Is the _____ sleeping in the cave?

5. How far is the moon from the _____?

6. Can you _____ what is in the box?

7. Would you like to ride in my _____ ship?

8. Will you stop _____ around now?

 At Home: Have your child suggest an answer to each question.

Little Bear Goes to the Moon
Book 1.5/Unit 6
 231

© Macmillan/McGraw-Hill

As you read Little Bear Goes to the Moon, fill in the Predictions Chart.

What I Predict	What Happens

How does the Predictions Chart help you better understand Little Bear Goes to the Moon?

At Home: Have your child use the chart to retell the story.

Name _____

Look at the picture. Read the sentence that tells what could happen next.

The dog will chase the ball.

Look at each picture. Underline the sentence that tells what could happen next.

1.

The boy will eat.

The boy will ride.

The boy will swim.

2.

She will plant flowers.

She will pick the flowers.

She will water the flowers.

3.

The ship will fly into space.

The ship will sail.

The ship will not go up.

4.

The dog will cut down the tree.

The cat will go up the tree.

The dog and cat will go to the lake.

© Macmillan/McGraw-Hill

 At Home: Ask your child to predict what will happen next in each story.

Little Bear Goes to the Moon
Book 1.5/Unit 6

 233

As I read, I will pay attention to the exclamation point.

	Bear sat in a tree.
5	He saw a funny bird in the sky.
13	Bear looked again. It was not a big bird.
22	It was a space ship.
27	And it landed on Earth.
32	Some people came out of it.
38	"I must tell Mother and Father," Bear said.
46	Bear went back to his den.
52	"Mother, Father!" he called.
56	"Guess what I saw today," he said. 63

Comprehension Check

1. What does Bear see?

2. Where are Mother and Father bear?

	Words Read	−	Number of Errors	=	Words Correct Score
First Read		−		=	
Second Read		−		=	

© Macmillan/McGraw-Hill

At Home: Help your child read the passage, paying attention to the goal at the top of the page.

Name _____

Use **context clues** to figure out the meaning of new words. Remember: Context clues may be found in the same sentence or in nearby sentences.

Use the <u>underlined</u> context clues to match the word in bold letters to its meaning.

1. Those <u>funny</u> <u>boys</u> are **fooling** around on the <u>playground</u>.

   A. something that protects a person's head

2. Ben <u>wears</u> a **helmet** and pretends to be an <u>astronaut</u> <u>driving</u> a <u>rocket</u>.

   B. the ground; also the planet where we live

3. Pete wears a cape and <u>pretends</u> to be a visitor from a <u>far-away</u> <u>star</u> in **space**.

   C. dropped, rolled

4. They <u>land</u> on the <u>hill</u> and **tumble** to the <u>ground</u>.

   D. joking, being silly

5. "It's great to <u>feel</u> the **earth** <u>under</u> my <u>feet</u> again," says Ben.

   E. the place where astronauts travel

© Macmillan/McGraw-Hill

 At Home: Ask your child to make up sentences using one of the words in bold letters.

Name _____

A **suffix** is a word part added to the end of a word. A suffix changes the meaning of the word.

The suffix -**ful** means **full of**.

help + **ful** = help**ful**

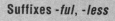

The suffix -**less** means **without**.

cloud + **less** = cloud**less**

Write -ful or -less to complete the word.

1. There are no trees on the hill. The hill is

_____

tree_____.

2. What nice flowers! How very

_____

thought_____ of you!

3. He held the tray without spilling.

_____

He was care_____.

4. There was no wind. The day was

_____

wind_____.

 At Home: Ask your child to use one of the words with the suffix -*less* or -*ful* in a sentence.

© Macmillan/McGraw-Hill

Name _____

The **question and answer format** uses the words **question** and **answer** to show who is speaking.

Question: How does it feel?

Answer: It feels like flying!

Draw a line to the person who is speaking.

1. Question: What should we make?

Answer: Let's make a pie.

2. Question: Where is my bat?

Answer: It is under the bed.

 At Home: Together, think of one more question and answer to go with one of the pictures on the page. Then write the question and answer using the question and answer format.

Little Bear Goes to the Moon
Book 1.5/Unit 6

 237

Read the words. The letters **ow, oo,** and **ou** stand for the vowel sound in **down, book,** and **clouds.**

She put d**ow**n the b**oo**k.
She saw the cl**ou**ds.

Write oo, ou or ow to complete each word.

1. c _____

2. noteb _____ k

3. r _____ nd

4. h _____ se

5. cl _____ n

6. f _____ tball

At Home: Have your child write two words that have the same vowel sound as clown. Do the same for book.

Name _____

The letters **oo** can stand for the middle sound in m**oo**n.
Read the words.

z**oo**   s**oo**n   t**oo**ls   m**oo**n

Write the letters <u>oo</u> to complete the words.
Draw a line from each picture to its name.

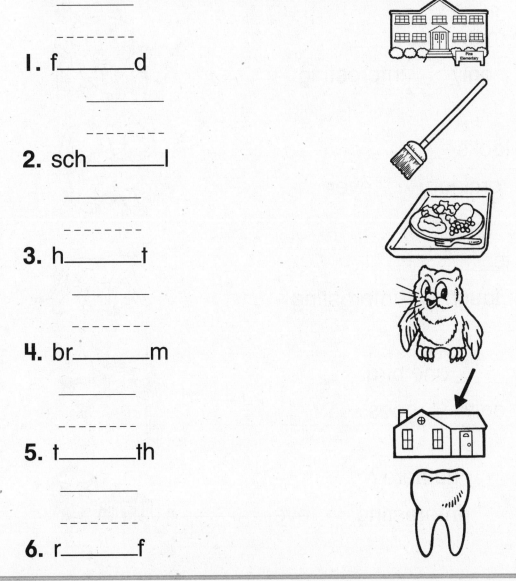

1. f_____d

2. sch_____l

3. h_____t

4. br_____m

5. t_____th

6. r_____f

At Home: Have your child brainstorm words with *oo* as in *moon*. As he or she thinks of a word, have your child write *oo* on a sheet of paper.

© Macmillan/McGraw-Hill

Name _____

only	laugh	goes
ever	ordinary	interesting

Circle the word that goes in each sentence.

1. The rocket _____ up.

   ever   goes   ordinary

2. She can make you _____.

   laugh   only   interesting

3. This cat looks _____.

   only   ordinary   ever

4. This cat is _____.

   goes   laugh   interesting

5. There is _____ one bird.

   ever   only   goes

6. Do you _____ go here?

   ordinary   interesting   ever

 At Home: Say the words in the box in random order. Have your child point to each word and say it in a sentence. Then point to the words for your child to read.

Name _____

As you read <u>Cool Jobs</u>, fill in the Classify and Catagorize Chart.

Classify and Categorize	
Jobs to Make Things	**Jobs That Help**

How does the Classify and Catagorize Chart help you better understand <u>Cool Jobs</u>?

At Home: Have your child use the chart to retell the story.

© Macmillan/McGraw-Hill

When you categorize and classify, you sort things into groups that are alike.

Circle the words for people.
Put an X on the words for animals.

boy	girl	bear
father	cat	mother
dog	bird	snake

Draw one of the people with one of the animals.
Write the group each is in.

 At Home: Have your child add a word to each category.

Name _____

Words with opposite meanings are **antonyms**. You can use a **thesaurus** to find an antonym for a word. **Antonyms** are listed after the **synonyms**.

loud   noisy, roaring   Antonym: **quiet**

small   little, tiny   Antonym: **big**

Read the sentence. Circle the antonym for the underlined word.

1. The <u>loud</u> lion looked out at us.

     quiet   little

2. We felt <u>small</u> as we looked back at her.

          hide   big

3. She had a <u>few</u> cubs.

        many   dull

4. We could <u>laugh</u> at the cubs.

          cry   blue

5. We were <u>glad</u> to be at the zoo.

        sad   many

 At Home: Ask your child to draw a picture that shows more about the sentences.

Name _____

As I read, I will pay attention to pauses for sentence punctuation.

	Pets can only show they are sick by
8	how they act.
11	Many sick animals hide. Some sick
17	pets do not eat their food.
23	A sick boy or girl goes to see the doctor.
33	A sick pet may see a doctor, too. The
42	doctor a pet sees is not an ordinary
50	doctor. She is a vet. 55

Comprehension Check

1. How do some sick animals act?

2. Who takes care of sick animals?

	Words Read	–	Number of Errors	=	Words Correct Score
First Read		–		=	
Second Read		–		=	

© Macmillan/McGraw-Hill

At Home: Help your student read the passage, paying attention to the goal at the top of the page.

Name _____

You can find out about anything on the Web! Put what you want to find in the search box. Hit GO. A list of websites will pop up.

○ ○ ○

◀ ▶ ⟳ + ☐ Look in the Media Center   ○ ⌕ ▾

📖   »

SEARCH | jobs | (GO)

Read the sentence.
Underline the word you would put in the search box.

1. You want to know more about a job with animals.

    animals   vet   birds

2. You want to find out about space.

    space   earth   farm

3. <u>Little Bear Goes to the Moon</u> is by Else Holmelund Minarik. You want to find out more about the author.

    bears   moon   Minarik

4. You want to find out about a kind of pet.

    bird   bear   bee

At Home: Think of other topics your child might want to research. Have your child tell the key words he or she would type into a search box.

Cool Jobs • Book 1.5/Unit 6

Name _____

Practice

Variant Vowel:
oo

Use the letters to make words. Match the words to the pictures.

b	d	f	l	m	n	p	r

____ ____

\- - - -   \- - - -

1. ___oo___

____ ____

\- - - -   \- - - -

2. ___oo___

____ ____

\- - - -   \- - - -

3. ___oo___

____ ____

\- - - -   \- - - -

4. ___oo___

____ ____

\- - - -   \- - - -

5. ___ ___oo___

____ ____

\- - - -   \- - - -

6. ___oo___

© Macmillan/McGraw-Hill

 At Home: Have your child make up a sentence using two of the words. Help your child to write the sentence.

Name _____

Read the questions. Write the answer.

1. Do you read a cook or a book?

_____

- -

_____

2. Do cows or owls moo?

_____

- -

_____

3. Is a log made of good or wood?

_____

- -

_____

4. Is a tooth found in a foot or a mouth?

_____

- -

_____

5. Do you eat with a spout or a spoon?

_____

- -

_____

6. Is "not up" down or gown?

_____

- -

_____

© Macmillan/McGraw-Hill

At Home: Say words with *ou, o͝o* or *o͞o* in sentences. Have your child write the letters that stand for the vowel sound.

Cool Jobs • **Book 1.5/Unit 6**

247

Read the words. What vowel sound do you hear?

The letters **au** or **aw** stand for the vowel sound in the words h**au**l and p**aw**.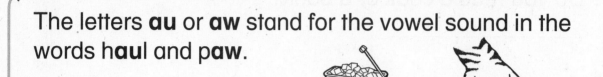

Circle the word that completes the sentence.

1. She can mow the _____.

lawn   yawn   dawn

2. We _____ the plane take off.

paw   saw   claw

3. He likes to _____.

paw   draw   flaw

4. This cat has _____.

saws   jaws   claws

 At Home: Have your child write one or two more words that have variant vowels: *au, aw*.

Circle a word to finish each sentence.

1. This _____ was just born.

    enough   cub   wild

2. Its _____ are closed.

    eyes   air   cub

3. The cub has a lot to _____.

    air   wild   learn

4. Soon it will be big _____ to walk.

    air   enough   eyes

5. The cub likes the spring _____.

    learn   across   air

6. It will hunt in the _____.

    wild   cub   enough

7. The cub wades _____ the stream.

    enough   across   learn

© Macmillan/McGraw-Hill

At Home: Have your child draw a picture of a bear cub and write a sentence about it. Ask your child to use this sentence starter: The cub will learn to _____.

A Tiger Cub Grows Up
Book 1.5/Unit 6

249

As you read <u>A Tiger Cub Grows Up</u>, fill in the Compare and Contrast Chart.

Compare and Contrast	
Cub	**Grown-up**

How does the Compare and Contrast Chart help you better understand <u>A Tiger Cub Grows Up</u>?

 At Home: Have your child use the chart to retell the story.

Name _____

When you **compare**, you tell how things are alike.

When you **contrast**, you tell how things are different.

Read the sentences.
If the sentence tells about Tara the tiger cub,
circle her picture.
If the sentence tells about the tiger from the poem,
circle the picture of the big tiger.
If the sentence tells about both animals, circle
both pictures.

I. I have baby teeth.

2. I see the vet.

3. I have many stripes.

4. I hunt in the forest.

 At Home: Have your child draw a picture of something both
tigers can do.

A Tiger Cub Grows Up
Book 1.5/Unit 6

 251

© Macmillan/McGraw-Hill

Name _____

As I read, I will pay attention to pauses for punctuation.

	How good are your eyes? Are they sharp
8	enough to spot a baby deer hiding?
15	Look!
16	A baby deer is not called a cub. It is called a
28	fawn. Baby deer are born in the spring.
36	The fawn has spots. The spotted coat will
44	help it hide. The fawn's mother is called a
53	doe. She has no spots. The fawn does not look
63	like its mother, yet. 67

Comprehension Check

1. What is a fawn?

2. When are baby deer born?

	Words Read	–	Number of Errors	=	Words Correct Score
First Read		–		=	
Second Read		–		=	

 At Home: Help your child read the passage, paying attention to the goal at the top of the page.

Name _____

An **inflected verb** is a verb with an ending. When you remove the **–ing** or **–ed** ending you are left with the base word.

inflected verb	base word
splash**ing**	splash
splash**ed**	splash

Cross out the ending. Then write the base word. The first one is done for you.

1. open~~ed~~   **open**

2. chewing _____

3. pointed _____

4. crawling _____

5. learning _____

6. talked _____

7. sleeping _____

8. tearing _____

At Home: As you read to your child, point out verbs ending in -ed and -ing. Ask your child to identify the base word.

Name _____

The letters **au** and **aw** stand
for the vowel sound
in P**au**l and s**aw**.

Choose a word from the box to finish each sentence.

yawns	crawl	caught	hawk	saw

1. At first the cubs _____.

2. One cub _____.

3. The other cub _____ a fish.

4. Then it _____ the fish.

5. A _____ flies away.

At Home: Have your child write one of the words from the
box in a sentence.

© Macmillan/McGraw-Hill

Name _____

Poets often use words in fun and interesting ways.
The sounds of words can help express the meaning.

Read the poem.
Circle the fun words in each verse.
Write the number words.

Race Starting

Bell horses, bell horses,
What time of day?
One o'clock, two o'clock,
Three and away.

One to make ready,
And two to prepare;
Good luck to the rider,
And away goes the mare.

One for the money,
Two for the show,
Three to make ready,
And four to go.

_____

- -

_____

_____

- -

_____

© Macmillan/McGraw-Hill

At Home: Have your child read the poem aloud with you.
Encourage your child to read the "fun words" from each verse
with expression that gives meaning to the words.

A Tiger Cub Grows Up
Book 1.5/Unit 6

255

The letters **au** and **aw** stand for the vowel sound in h**au**l and p**aw**.

The letters **oo** can stand for the vowel sound in l**oo**k.

The letters **oo** can also stand for the vowel sound in f**oo**d.

Circle the word that names the picture.

1. spark   spoon   spook

2. book   boost   brook

3. paw   dawn   pause

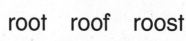

4. root   roof   roost

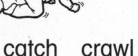

5. cook   catch   crawl

6. brook   book   boost

© Macmillan/McGraw-Hill

At Home: Have your child sort the words on the page into three groups according to their vowel sounds.

Name _____

Read the words. The letters **oy** and **oi** stand for the sounds in b**oy** and b**oil**.

b**oy** 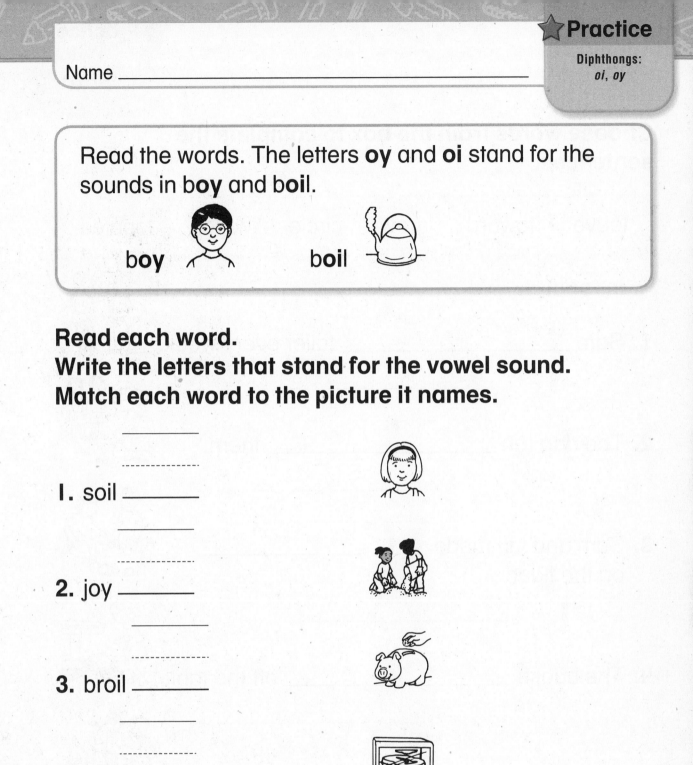   b**oil**

Read each word.
Write the letters that stand for the vowel sound.
Match each word to the picture it names.

1. soil _____

2. joy _____

3. broil _____

4. toy _____

5. coin _____

 At Home: Have your child write sentences using the words
on the page.

Choose words from the box to complete the sentences.

| leave | toward | grew | circle | wreck | toppled |

1. Sam _____ taller every week.

2. The dog ran _____ them.

3. Sam and Lin made _____ on the floor.

4. The books _____ off the table.

5. Oh, no! The dog will _____ all our hard work.

6. Let's _____ a note for Max.

© Macmillan/McGraw-Hill

At Home: Ask your child to use two of the words in sentences.

Name _____

As you read <u>Sand Castle</u>, fill in the Cause and Effect Chart.

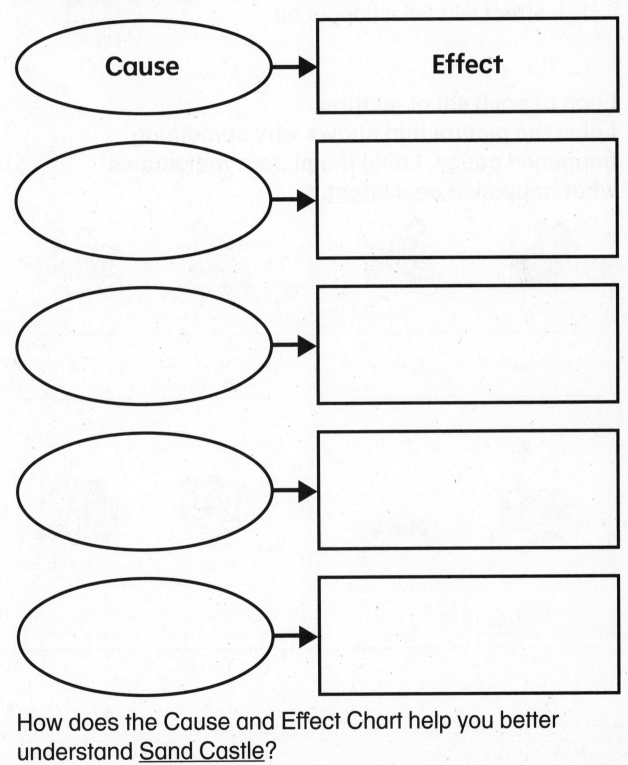

Cause → **Effect**

How does the Cause and Effect Chart help you better understand <u>Sand Castle</u>?

 At Home: Have your child use the chart to retell the story.

Name _____

The **cause** tells why something happened.
The **effect** tells what happened.

Look at each set of pictures.
Label the picture that shows why something
happened <u>cause</u>. **Label the picture that shows**
what happened next <u>effect</u>.

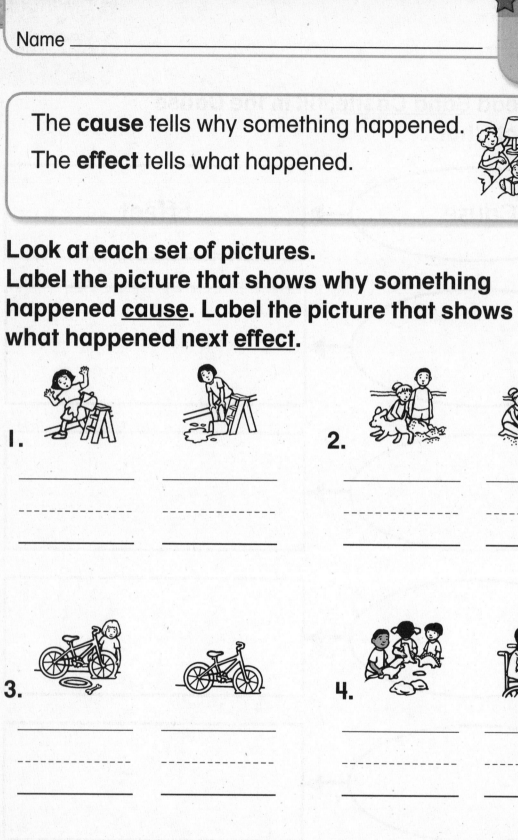

1.

2.

3.

4.

 At Home: Have your child make up a story about one of the
picture sequences.

© Macmillan/McGraw-Hill

As I read, I will pay attention to the question.

	"This is Carlos," she said. "Join me in welcoming him
10	to our class."
13	"Hello, Carlos," the children said together.
19	"Carlos is from Spain," said Miss Kent. "He speaks only
29	a little English. We all have to help him learn more."
40	Then Miss Kent read to the children. Andy looked over
50	toward Carlos. Would Carlos like to play outside with
59	him? Andy could help him speak English. 66

Comprehension Check

1. Where is Carlos from?

2. What will the children help Carlos learn?

	Words Read	−	Number of Errors	=	Words Correct Score
First Read		−		=	
Second Read		−		=	

At Home: Help your child read the passage, paying attention to the goal at the top of the page.

Context clues are words that help you figure out the meaning of a new word. Context clues may be found in the same sentence or in nearby sentences.

Fill in the circle next to the correct meaning for the word in <u>bold letters</u>. Use the <u>underlined</u> context clues to help you figure out the correct meaning.

1. Carl digs a <u>moat</u> to <u>protect</u> the <u>castle</u> from **danger**.

   O a tall tower   O harm or risk

2. <u>Water</u> <u>filled</u> the moat when the **bucket** fell over.

   O rained   O a pail

3. His dog **gazes** <u>at</u> the moving water <u>closely</u>.

   O to watch or stare   O traps

4. Dad <u>watches</u> Carl and <u>smiles</u> **proudly**.

   O friendly   O in a happy way

At Home: Ask your child to tell a story about a castle. Encourage the use of at least two words in bold letters in the story.

© Macmillan/McGraw-Hill

Name _____

**Blend the sounds and say the word.
Write the word.
Match each word to the picture it names.**

_____

- - - - - - - - - - - - - - - -

1. b   oi   l = _____

_____

- - - - - - - - - - - - - - - -

2. c   oi   n = _____

_____

- - - - - - - - - - - - - - - -

3. b   oy = _____

_____

- - - - - - - - - - - - - - - -

4. br   oi   l = _____

_____

- - - - - - - - - - - - - - - -

5. t   oy = _____

_____

- - - - - - - - - - - - - - - -

6. oi   l = _____

© Macmillan/McGraw-Hill

At Home: Have your child write one more word that has the
same vowel sound as *boy* or *boil*.

Sand Castle • Book 1.5/Unit 6

Name _____

Captions tell you facts about a photo or picture.

Pam and Mike
at the beach, June 28.

Use the captions to answer the questions.

Jen and Tim make a house.
Max watches.

1. Who are the children ?

   Jen and Tom   Pam and Mike   Jen and Tim

2. What are the children doing?

   making a town   making a car   making a house

3. Who is watching the children?

   Sam   Max   Mike

Mike and his friends make
a town out of clay.

4. Who are the children?

   Matt and friends   Sam and friends   Mike and friends

5. What are the children doing?

   making a town   making a house   making a wall

At Home: Have your child draw a picture of children
building something out of blocks. Together, make up a
caption for the drawing.

© Macmillan/McGraw-Hill

Name _____

Use the letters <u>oi</u> or <u>oy</u> to complete the words.

1. We need more _____ l for the car.

2. Jen put the plants in the s _____ l.

3. Bill likes to hit his t _____ drum.

4. Mom has to b _____ l more water.

5. The b _____ is washing his dog.

 At Home: Ask your child to look through magazines and catalogs for pictures of words that have short *u* sounds, short *o* sounds, and the same diphthong sound as in *boy*.

Sand Castle • Book 1.5/Unit 6   265

Name _____

Circle the picture that tells about the words.

1. wild bear

2. space helmet

 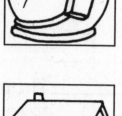

3. interesting house

4. searching for clues

5. grew big with air

Circle the word that completes each sentence.

1. Jokes make
_____

----

me _____.

guess   laugh

2. Roy sits across
_____

----

the _____.

table   toward

3. The
_____

_____ are wild.

eyes   birds

4. We
_____

_____ to read.

leave   learn

5. Paul
_____

_____ to school.

goes   gone

6. There is only
_____

----

one _____.

other   circle